JET FIGHTERS

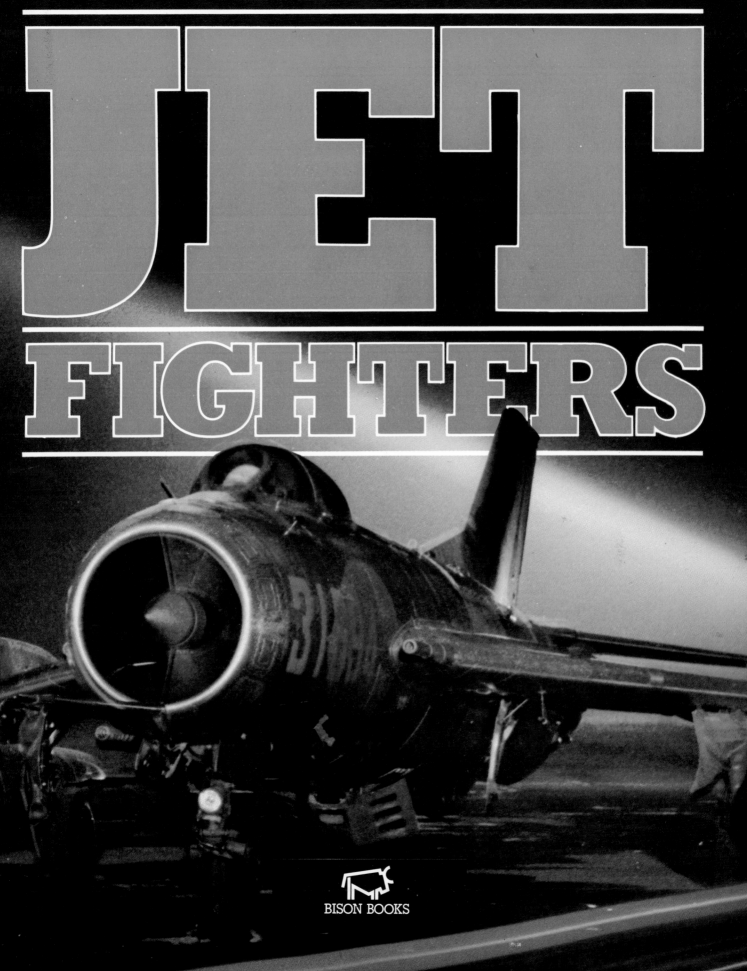

MICHAEL TAYLOR

JET FIGHTERS

BISON BOOKS

This edition published by
Bison Books Limited
17 Sherwood Place, Greenwich,
Connecticut 06830, USA

Copyright © 1982 Bison Books Limited

ISBN 0-86124-088-X

Printed in Hong Kong.

CONTENTS

1: AGAINST THE ODDS

Turbojet and turbofan-powered fighters of today are man-made meteors of destruction; the most formidable are capable of speeds of more than two-and-a-half times the speed of sound and possess incredible rates of climb of approximately 50,000 feet per minute. In a secondary attack role, the same fighters can carry bombs and other weapons equivalent in weight to that carried by some of the heaviest bombers of World War II. All this is a far cry from the first jet fighters that appeared in operational units in 1944.

It seems incongruous that jet fighters were streaking in the skies of Europe during World War II, but no more so than the USAF finding in some situations during the Vietnam conflict that high-technology multi-million dollar jet fighter-bombers were of less use than veteran piston-engined aircraft. Such are the unexpected demands of war. What is surprising is that despite the appalling amount of time wasted in getting jets into service during World War II, between the time the Luftwaffe received its first jets and its capitulation Germany produced more than ten 'jet aces.' Oberstleutnant Heinz Bär of JV 44, the Luftwaffe's elite jet squadron formed in early 1945 by Adolf Galland, personally boasted no fewer than 16 'jet kills' amongst his overall war total of 220 victories.

It is a common misconception to believe that jet fighters were the end result for Germany and Britain of frantic experiments prior to the outbreak of war, to lay the foundations for the ultimate warplane. Far from it. Whilst it is true that there were those in both countries that had faith in the gas turbine engine as a power plant for aircraft, official government views were far from encouraging, as is now explained.

Three names are synonymous with the early development of the turbojet engine and turbojet-powered aircraft, those of Whittle, von Ohain and Heinkel. But whilst Whittle was the first to run a turbojet engine intended as a power plant for an aircraft, the Germans were the first to marry engine and airframe. This came about not because the German Air Ministry had any more faith in the concept than the British Air Ministry, but because von Ohain had the help of an airframe manufacturer whereas Whittle had not.

In Germany in the 1930s Ernst Heinkel was the head of a major aircraft manufacturing company, Ernst Heinkel Flugzeugwerke GmbH. He believed that no piston-engined aircraft would ever exceed around

Above: the Heinkel He 178, which was the world's first jet-powered aircraft, lifts off.

Overleaf: this Gloster F.9/40 Meteor was powered by Rolls-Royce Trent turboprops.

800 km/h (500 mph). A similar view was taken by eminent persons in Britain. Typical was the stance adopted by a former British Director of Scientific Research in a lecture he gave in early 1937, when he stated that higher speeds could be attained only if a new 'prime mover' was invented producing much greater thrust, and that there was no inkling of such a power plant and man would probably never exceed 965 km/h (600 mph) level speed in an aeroplane. By the time of this lecture Whittle and the staff of Power Jets Ltd had already run the first Whittle turbojet engine!

Going further back to 1926, a Briton named Dr A A Griffith expounded his ideas on gas turbine engines for aeroplanes. He was then employed at the Royal Aircraft Establishment (RAE). In the same year a young man named Frank Whittle joined the RAF College at Cranwell as a Flight Cadet. Two years later an article entitled *Speculation* appeared in the college journal, in which Whittle gave an outline of the equations for a gas turbine engine. While at the Central Flying School in 1929 he had a meeting with officials at the Air Ministry, who it is said considered his ideas impracticable. Sensibly, Whittle took out a patent to protect his brainchild but then settled down to his chosen career, although he made further attempts to interest the Air Ministry. One outcome of these meetings was that the

Ministry was coerced into supporting limited research at the RAE, which in the event achieved virtually nothing.

If one looks at the list of directors for the later-formed company Power Jets (Research and Development) Ltd, three of the names are Whittle, J C B Tinling and R D Williams. Tinling and Williams had been RAF officers and knew of Whittle's work. By 1935 they had together established an engineering business and felt in a position to approach Whittle with a proposition that was to lead eventually to the greatest sustained leap forward in aviation technology since the invention of the internal combustion engine. They suggested that for a share of the profits they would attempt to find the necessary finance to build a Whittle engine. A company named Power Jets Ltd was formed, with the intention of producing an engine suited for a revolutionary stratospheric mailplane. About the same time the Air Ministry was taking more interest in the type of engine, via the RAE, having changed its mind about the jet engine's possible military applications.

Whittle began serious design in mid-1935 and the first Whittle engine with a centrifugal compressor, known as the W/U Type, was built by the British Thomson-Houston Company, based at Rugby, to a Power Jets order. This engine was the first gas turbine engine to be designed for an aircraft and, amid great excitement, was started up for the first time on 12 April 1937, several months prior to the von Ohain engine in Germany.

Now work really began in earnest. Soon the W/U was being modified and reconstructed, running again in very different form in October 1938. The W/U was

Above: the Power Jets W1 engine mounted on a test stand at Lutterworth, Leicestershire.

Whittle's only engine until the W1X was started up in December 1940 and all jet development up to this time by Power Jets was carried out on this single unit. In March 1938 the Air Ministry placed a contract for a Whittle engine. The Ministry later awarded Gloster a contract to produce an airframe to carry the engine under specification E.28/39.

Meanwhile in Germany by the mid-1930s unusual experiments were also taking place. As mentioned earlier, Ernst Heinkel was a leader in the development of the German turbojet engine, but he also had an important role to play in the development of a rocket motor for aircraft. Indeed Heinkel was initially involved with rocket power and saw a great future for this type of power plant. For Heinkel, what his rocket-powered aircraft experiments proved was that a rear-exhausting power plant was feasible for aeroplanes, against the official German Air Ministry viewpoint. But, as if by retribution for not toeing the line, his engines never achieved any major production success and other companies more successfully exploited turbojet and rocket-powered aircraft for operational use with the Luftwaffe.

In late 1935 Ernst Heinkel met a young scientist named Wernher von Braun, who had been experimenting with rocket motors for the German Army at Kummersdorf. Such was the eventual success of his experiments that between December of the following year and 1938 the 'whole show' was officially moved from Kummersdorf to the new highly secret and much larger research establishment built for the Third Reich at Peenemünde, where the 'terror weapons' of World War II were developed.

Heinkel had not been requested to visit Kummersdorf to admire von Braun's work on artillery rocket motors, but to hear his ideas for a rocket-powered plane. Why Heinkel had been selected from all the heads of German airframe manufacturers to be approached can be explained easily. Firstly he had expounded openly his criticism of German engine manufacturers, who in his opinion were falling behind in technological progress when compared with the achievements being made in other European countries. Secondly von Braun had already tested rocket engines on a rig, which had rotated at great speed before exploding, and he now wanted one of the most modern aeroplane fuselages with which to continue his work towards a rocket plane, and Heinkel had such a fuselage.

At this time the Heinkel company had flown the prototype of its new He 112 single-seat monoplane fighter, a rival for the Messerschmitt Bf 109 for Luftwaffe orders and von Braun modestly wanted an He 112 fuselage. Luckily for him, he had approached the right man. Under intense secrecy Ernst Heinkel provided an He 112 fuselage, together with a number of Heinkel employees.

During the first weeks of 1936 von Braun tested his motor installed in the anchored fuselage, all trials being conducted for safety from behind a concrete wall screen. The liquid oxygen and alcohol tanks to fuel the motor were placed fore and aft of the cockpit. With von Braun behind the wall was Erich Warsitz, who had already volun-

teered to fly a rocket-powered plane when developed. What he must have felt when one explosion followed another can only be speculated upon, but, as will be explained, Warsitz was later very important to rocket and turbojet-powered aircraft research and development.

By February von Braun felt that he had developed the motor to a point where it was safe for onlookers to stand beside the fuselage while the motor was run and he and Warsitz did this daring act to impress Ernst Heinkel. Luckily it did impress him, for von Braun was soon in need of a second fuselage when the first had blown up with a motor during later tests. This too was subsequently destroyed. The third He 112 provided was a complete aircraft. Once with von Braun it had a rocket motor installed in the aft fuselage. It was envisioned that in this aircraft Warsitz was to attempt a few simple rocket motor tests while airborne, but it too exploded. Still Warsitz retained faith in the concept, and, after von Braun had extracted yet another He 112 out of Heinkel, he realised his dream.

In April 1937 the second complete He 112 took off under the power of its piston engine, but switched to rocket power once airborne. With tremendous acceleration the plane's speed rose. Then the cockpit became filled with fumes and Warsitz made an emergency crash landing. In the following period the repaired He 112 flew several times, eventually taking off under rocket power alone.

During 1937 von Braun released details of his experiments and those of others in the same field to the Air Ministry. A motor fed with a different fuel mixture had by then been produced by Walter. This motor was also tested in the He 112 and proved very successful. In fact the Walter motor was the forerunner of the type later installed in the operational Messerschmitt Me 163 Komet rocket interceptor.

Much to Ernst Heinkel's dismay, the aeroplane rocket motor concept was seen by German officials mainly as a RATO (rocket-assisted take-off) unit for heavily-laden bombers and not as the main power plant for an aeroplane. Whilst Heinkel also saw its use in this role, especially in view of his own bombers being built for the Luftwaffe, it went against his main line of thinking. What is more, he had eyes on the world speed record for aeroplanes. Therefore, he subsequently offered von Braun and Warsitz a purpose-built rocket plane airframe, made small enough to win the record by a wide margin. Naturally this was greeted with

great enthusiasm, and the He 176 was built. Aiming for 1,000 km/h, it was designed to have a pilot escape capsule in case of an emergency.

As time passed von Braun became deeply involved with artillery rockets at Peenemünde and began to show less interest in the He 176. Not so the pilot, Warsitz. When completed the He 176 was taken in sections to the research establishment and later went through a series of towed and taxi trials and then hops. Then in June 1939 Warsitz made a 50 second flight without mishap. The next flight was in front of Ernst Heinkel, Ernst Udet, Erhard Milch and other dignitaries. A stop-go attitude from the General Staff followed, with the He 176 and Warsitz in turn forbidden to fly.

It soon became clear that the General Staff saw the He 176 as little more than a toy, with perhaps some future in developed form as a vertically-launched rocket interceptor to destroy bombers. Heinkel was again frustrated. History records that in fact Germany did eventually develop several rocket-powered interceptors for use during World War II, although Heinkel did not get a look-in. One has already been mentioned, but another of great interest was the Bachem Ba 349 Natter, which was indeed vertically launched. As for the He 176, it was destroyed alongside the He 178 during an Allied bombing raid on Berlin, where it had been sent for the Air Museum.

The He 178 itself was the outcome of very different experiments which ran parallel with those of the He 176. In 1936 Ernst Heinkel had again been contacted about another new type of power plant. Contact had come from Professor Robert Pohl of the University of Göttingen. He explained that he had a 24-year-old colleague named Hans Joachim Pabst von Ohain who was working on the design of a turbojet engine. On later meeting von Ohain, Heinkel was most impressed with his theories. But, although a

Above: a rare photograph of the Gloster E.28/39 experimental jet aircraft during flight trials.

model had previously been produced for von Ohain by Bartels and Beckers garage, von Ohain was not an engineer and had spent most of his private money thus far.

In April von Ohain and his assistant Max Hahn joined the Heinkel company. They worked in a specially-prepared building well away from the main Heinkel manufacturing plant at Marienehe, to maintain strict secrecy. Ernst Heinkel was very enthusiastic about this project and allowed many of his best employees to work with von Ohain and Hahn, together with a number of new employees. In the event, much of the detail work on the engine was left to Hahn.

Development of the turbine and the combustion chamber for the hydrogen fuel took about a year and a half. Following a number of unsuccessful attempts to run the engine, the S.1 started up for the first time in September 1937, well after Whittle's engine in Britain. This engine was designed for developmental purposes only and had a thrust of just 80kg (176lb). It was followed by the S.2 with a thrust of 130kg (286lb). By the

spring of 1938 the remarkable S.3 engine had been developed, which was fed with petrol and was controllable. In fact two S.3 series engines were built.

The S.3 was based on a compressor/turbine arrangement, comprising an axial-flow inducer, axial-flow impeller and radial inflow turbine. In this the air from the axial-flow impeller was divided to the rear of the diffuser; some passed forward through the annular reverse-flow combustion chamber and the rest was directed rearward to mix with the combustion gases before entry into the turbine. Total weight of the unit was 360kg (794lb), and its frontal area was 0.68 sq m (7.3 sq ft). The latter figure was important as Heinkel intended it to be mounted inside a small-diameter fuselage. There was some disagreement as to this installation, as it was realised that the engine's possible 450kg (992lb) of thrust would be reduced significantly if a long air intake and jetpipe were adopted, as would be necessary with the engine in the fuselage. Nevertheless Heinkel won the day, the purpose-built turbojet-powered research aircraft was to be a single-engined type.

Prior to flying the purpose-built He 178, the S.3 was flight tested on another aircraft. Here there is some confusion. Ernst Heinkel recorded much later that the first S.3 was fitted to an He 118 for initial flight testing and this appears to be generally accepted. The He 118 was the Heinkel entry for the latest dive-bomber competition, which incidentally was won by the Junkers Ju 87. This seemingly unlikely choice of engine test-bed may have resulted from its availability and/or its good ground clearance by virtue of having been expected to carry a large bomb under the fuselage. However others

Below: a Gloster F.9/40 prototype pictured at Farnborough, Hampshire, in 1944.

Right: a Power Jets W2 jet engine is pictured installed in the Gloster E.28/39 airframe.

that worked on this early engine mention its installation in an He 100 single-seat fighter. The He 100 was basically a development of the He 112, as used for the rocket plane experiments, and in some respects seems at first a more likely choice. With the He 118 the engine would have had to be mounted beneath the fuselage. Although it is possible that the He 100 was used after initial flights with the He 118, no certainty can be expressed. However the He 100 would have allowed Heinkel and the others to measure actual reductions in thrust due to the use of an air intake and a jetpipe of some length.

By the time that the He 178 airframe had been completed in secrecy, the first engine's turbine had burned out. As there were only two engines, the decision was made to fit the remaining S.3b engine to the He 178 without delay.

The He 178 was not dissimilar in many ways to the He 176, although there were important differences apart from engine type. The nose of the duralumin-constructed monocoque fuselage had a large air intake, through which air was directed under the cramped pilot's cockpit to the engine installed approximately level with the trailing-edge of the shoulder-mounted wooden wings. A long jetpipe of welded chrome steel exhausted out of the rear fuselage. As with the He 176, the tailwheel-type landing gear was retractable.

Naturally there was only one pilot suited to the job of flying the He 178, not least because Warsitz had already been the pilot during the earlier-mentioned testbed flights. Warsitz had shown exceptional faith in Heinkel's experimental aircraft and had flown all of the earlier rocket and turbojet trials with great fortitude. Even the General Staff, who had not exactly been at pains to praise Heinkel for his private-venture contributions to the advancement of German aviation, had recognized Warsitz's great courage. Indeed it had organized large payments for his hazardous flights. Nevertheless even Warsitz was not entirely happy with the choice of the Marienehe airfield for flight testing the He 178. For a start he considered the airfield too short. Yet to go elsewhere would break the secrecy of their work and could conceivably cause the premature termination of the whole project. Of course, one of the Air Ministry's complaints – that engines should be made by engine makers – had already been settled by

Heinkel, for he acquired a major interest in the Hirth-Motoren engine company after the death of Hellmuth Hirth in June 1938.

Taxiing trials with the He 178 began on 24 August 1939. Then on 27 August Warsitz climbed into the small cockpit and was soon streaking along the airfield. Suddenly the aircraft left the ground and powered its way upwards. Unlike his flight in the He 176, Warsitz stayed up for minutes rather than seconds, to record the first flight in the world of a turbojet-powered aeroplane. History had indeed been made and those watching the flight knew it.

Ernst Heinkel's enthusiasm for the group's achievement was not matched by the response of Ernst Udet of the German Air Ministry (RLM), who had been contacted directly. Heinkel wanted him to see the second flight of the He 178 and could not understand why there should be any delay whatsoever. Actually the reason was simple, for it was only hours before German forces were to invade Poland. It was not until 1 November that Udet, Milch and Lucht visited the airfield to see the He 178's second flight; Goering had not even turned up. That day the first flight was a disaster, as it had to be terminated immediately after take off because of a seized fuel pump. Within three hours the fault had been rectified and a full demonstration was put on. Although the officials showed little interest as they departed, at least Heinkel now had a clearer idea of what he was going to be up against if he was to proceed.

When the Allies took charge of documents following Germany's capitulation in 1945, references were found for an S.6 engine, which preceded the important S.8 or 109-001. This was merely a new designation given to the S.3b prior to the November flights and following modifications to the engine to raise static thrust to 590kg (1301lb). However it appears to have

achieved poor results due to an increase in weight to 420kg (929lb). It is interesting to note that despite Heinkel's early lead, the company produced only a very small number of von Ohain engines in the projected S.1, S.2, S.3, S.8 and S.11 series, whilst the ducted fan engines designed by Max Mueller (who joined Heinkel from Junkers) as the S.50 and S.60 remained projects, as did his S.40. Mueller's S.30 axial-flow engine, known as the 109-006, was intended for the He 280 but was abandoned for some unexplainable reason after very great progress had been made. As for the He 178, this was destroyed alongside the He 176 in Berlin.

Although other German turbojet engines are mentioned later in this book, it is interesting to note at this point that BMW began preliminary work on jet propulsion in 1934 and commenced design of its 109-003 engine in 1939, which ran in the summer of the following year. The 109-003 had a seven-stage axial compressor and an annular combustion chamber with 16 burners and was the first type of turbojet fitted to a prototype Messerschmitt Me 262. Similarly Professor Leist at Daimler-Benz first ran a 109-007 in the autumn of 1943, but work was eventually abandoned as the engine was seen to be too complex by the German Air Ministry. The -007 had many special features, including the compressor and ducted fan being mounted on two contra-rotating drums. By far the most successful turbojet of German origin was the Junkers Jumo 109-004. Junkers had begun development in 1937, having been encouraged to so do by the technical division at the Air Ministry, and within two years the design for a turbojet engine had been completed. Construction of the prototype Jumo 109-004 began in 1940 and the first was started up in November that year. By mid-1941 Junkers had a number of engines completed. Towards the end of 1941 the Jumo 004 was flight tested by a Messerschmitt Bf 110. At about that time certain modifications to the engine had been designed to produce the 109-004B, which was run in late 1942. Meanwhile on 18 July 1942, -004As had been used in a prototype Me 262.

In Britain Power Jets had used considerable ingenuity in developing its W1 engine for flight trials in the Gloster E.28/39 airframe and, by making use of spare W1 component parts and others that were considered below standard for the flight engine, the company produced a second engine as the non-airworthy W1X. Interestingly, the W1X was the first of the two engines to be started up. It was to be used to help Gloster prepare the installation for the airworthy W1 and so successful was it that the initial taxiing trials of the E.28/39 were made with the W1X installed.

At this point one of aviation's remarkable but unrecognised 'firsts' occurred. Although the engine had a rating of 454kg (1,000lb) thrust, for safety this was to be kept down to 390kg (860lb). The pilot for the E.28/39 was PEG Sayer, Gloster's Chief Test Pilot. On 7 April 1941 Sayer performed the first taxiing trial, but on the following day he made the first of a number of 'hop' flights, still with the W1X engine fitted. As in the earliest days of flying, 'hop' flights were not counted as true flights and therefore, although Britain's first turbojet-powered aeroplane had left the ground, it was not a recorded 'first.'

The E.28/39 was then dismantled and taken to Cranwell, where it was to make its first proper flight with the W1 engine fitted. No doubt Whittle was pleased with this location, as Cranwell was where the jet engine was conceived and now would be the place of its fulfilment. As for the W1X, it was sent to the General Electric Company in the United States of America in September 1941, where it helped that company develop its own engine to power the first US jet fighter.

At 7.40 pm on 15 May 1941 Sayer took off in the E.28/39, making a highly successful 17 minute flight in which a speed of 386 km/h (240 mph) was recorded. This marked the first flight of a turbojet-powered aircraft anywhere in the world outside Germany. So successful was the engine/airframe combination that flying was cleared for ten hours with only routine attention. In fact during 17 flights without failure, up to 28 May, this was marginally exceeded. Within one and a half months the W1 was run on a Special Category Test of 25 hours and then it was again flight tested.

Right: an Avro Lancaster flight tests an F.2 turbojet engine mounted in the bomber's tail.

Whilst the British Air Ministry had not shown very much initiative earlier, now that Britain was at war it took much greater interest in jet propulsion. Even before the E.28/39 had flown, the Air Ministry had placed contracts for new engines and a prototype twin-engined fighter as the F.9/40. In June 1940 Dr Harold Roxbee Cox was appointed Deputy Director of Scientific Research with responsibility for the development of gas turbine engines.

Up to then Power Jets' engines had been built by the British Thomson-Houston Company. The new W2 engine for the Air Ministry was to have a thrust of 726kg (1600lb) and it was optimistically hoped by the Air Ministry that large numbers of these engines and fighter aircraft airframes could be coming off production lines very quickly.

As Britain and Germany appeared to be on the verge of producing jet fighters in 1940, why did it take until 1944 to get them into service? The answer to this is in the following chapter, which covers the actual development of jet fighter prototypes and production aircraft. It is sufficient here to say that turbojet engine development did not keep pace with airframe development. Indeed, in Britain Power Jets had tremendous difficulty developing the W2, which suffered compressor surging, turbine blade failure and other problems. Meanwhile the Rover Company had tooled for production and had to sit by while the small band of Power Jets workers at Lutterworth struggled to solve the problems.

Rover itself attempted to rectify the faults by carrying out modifications to the engine, which actually achieved little. Soon strain between Rover and Power Jets showed, but in an epic moment of aviation history Rolls-Royce offered to take over Rovers' turbojet activities at Barnoldswick in exchange for its own tank engine factory at Nottingham. Of course Rolls-Royce were aware of what it was taking on, for it had already given some assistance to Power Jets. Rolls-Royce was now in the turbojet industry.

Virtually as soon as the agreement had been struck between Rover and Rolls-Royce, and before Rolls-Royce took over the Barnoldswick factory in early 1943, Rolls-Royce had converted a Vickers Wellington bomber into a flying testbed for the Whittle engine, which now carried the

designation W.2B/23 and had a thrust of 567kg (1250lb). The engine was mounted in the Wellington's tail, with the turret removed and 25 hours of flying was performed, from the end of 1942. A second Wellington was also modified for high-altitude work.

The initial Rolls-Royce version of the W.2B/23 passed its 100 hour test in April 1943, the same month as Rolls-Royce officially took over the Barnoldswick factory. This engine was capable of 771kg (1700lb) thrust. Production deliveries of the Welland engine, as it was now named, began in May 1944. Rolls-Royce had always expected Barnoldswick to be mainly a research and development establishment, with the bulk of production to take place at Newcastle-under-Lyme, and indeed only 100 or so engines were built there.

The Rolls-Royce Derwent engine, intended as a Welland replacement, was based on the Rover W.2B/26, itself modelled on a Power Jets direct-flow combustion engine. The W.2B/26 first ran in March 1942 and the Rolls-Royce Derwent I development ran in July 1943, giving a thrust of 907kg (2000lb). The company's Nene engine, which was designed and built in just five and a half months, first ran on 27 October 1944. It was designed to give a static thrust of 1814kg (4000lb) but was improved for flying at 2268kg (5000lb) thrust. An American-built Lockheed P-80 Shooting Star was adapted as this engine's testbed. Perhaps the oddest installation of the period was when a prototype Meteor was used to flight test the Rolls-Royce Trent engine, which was similar to the Derwent but drove a five-blade propeller.

As in Germany, once the advantages of the turbojet engine had been realized, other companies entered the field, the most important of which were de Havilland and Metropolitan-Vickers. The former began design of what became the H-1 or Goblin in April 1941, and by March 1943 the engine was flying in a prototype Meteor. On 20 September it powered the D.H.100 Vampire jet fighter prototype on its maiden flight. Metropolitan-Vickers started turbojet development much earlier, in fact in 1938, and by 1940 had designed its F.2 axial-flow turbojet engine. Flight tests in a converted Lancaster began on 29 June 1943, followed by tests in a prototype Meteor from 13 November. Thrust for the F.2/1 was 816kg (1800lb).

As for Power Jets Ltd., the company that had started the ball rolling in Britain, it be-came voluntarily state owned in 1944, thereafter being known as Power Jets (Research and Development) Ltd. On 1 July 1946 the roles of this company, which were purely research and developmental and not to manufacture, were passed to the National Gas Turbine Establishment, which also took over its buildings. The head of the former Power Jets organisation, Roxbee Cox, became head of this Establishment. It was the end of an era. Some say jet engine development began as long ago as 1910, when the Romanian Henri Coanda is said to have flown briefly in a biplane powered by a 50hp Clerget piston engine which drove a fan in a nose duct to produce thrust. It actually began with Whittle's experiments and was now a reality. Meanwhile in 1943 the development of the jet fighter was still in its infancy.

2: THE FIRST JET FIGHTERS

Heinkel was undoubtedly the prewar champion of the German turbojet engine and jet aeroplane and he should have been in a strong position to monopolize both during World war II. Although by 1939 some members of the RLM had adopted a more realistic approach to the development of the turbojet and turbojet-powered aircraft, in the main the ministry remained convinced that there was no real need, or future, for either. But, in order to hedge its bets, it had by then encouraged other engine makers to develop turbojets. It also unknowingly further usurped Heinkel by giving the company a rival in the airframe field. The latter was Messerschmitt AG, which as early as 1938 had been contracted to produce a preliminary design for a twin-engined jet plane. How serious the RLM was at that time in wanting such an aeroplane can perhaps be judged only by its reaction to the flights of the He 178. However the new aeroplane was seen merely as an engine test-bed. The Messerschmitt design was known as Project 1065.

The reason that the RLM favored Messerschmitt was to be found partly in the fact that Heinkel kept its experiments a close secret until success had been achieved. This attitude seemed expedient to Ernst Heinkel, who considered his experiments always under threat of premature shut-down, but on the other hand must have gone some way in blinding the RLM to the advanced nature of his company's work, as well as building mistrust.

Although intended as a test-bed, Messerschmitt had been quick to point out the Project 1065's suitability as a prototype jet fighter. Heinkel was also working on the design of a prototype fighter and, like Project 1065, adopted a twin underwing jet engine arrangement. In the first half of 1940 Messerschmitt and Heinkel received contracts to produce a small number of flying and static test aircraft for fighter development, although official attitudes at the RLM, and especially those of Udet and Milch, remained virtually unchanged. Only after the Luftwaffe had received a 'bloody nose' during the Battle of Britain did the RLM realize once and for all that long term development of warplanes was going to be

essential; superior numbers had not won the day and there was not going to be a quick end to the war.

Heinkel appeared in a happier position than Messerschmitt by virtue of having two engines under development that were suited to the new aeroplane, now designated He 280. The first was von Ohain's S.8 centrifugal-flow engine; the second was Mueller's S.30 axial-flow engine. The first He 280 airframe was ready well before the S.8 engines and so it was used in a series of unpowered flights to gauge its aerodynamic qualities. An He 111 was used to tow the He 280 into the air. Many such unpowered flights were made while von Ohain and his team tried desperately to develop the S.8 to a point where sufficient thrust was produced to power the He 280 successfully and reliably.

Although the S.8 had been intended to produce 700kg (1543lb) of thrust, by the time 500kg (1102lb) was achieved the decision was made to fit two to the first He 280 airframe, under its straight but tapering wings. On 2 April 1941 the He 280V1 took off for the first time, with the nacelle panels for the engines removed as they tended to collect dangerous leaking fuel. This flight marked not only the first flight of a twin-engined turbojet-powered aircraft, but the

Overleaf: the Lockheed P-80 Shooting Star first flew on 8 January 1944, the XP-80A being pictured.

Below: Germany's Messerschmitt Me 262 saw combat service at the end of World War II.

Above: the Messerschmitt Me 262B-1a was a two-seat jet fighter trainer from which a nightfighter was developed.

first of a turbojet-powered machine intended as a fighter prototype. Often ignored is the fact that this flight *preceded* that of the experimental British Gloster E.28/39. What is more, the He 280 had several other very advanced features, which included a compressed air ejection seat for the pilot, and preempted the later Me 262 by having a tricycle landing gear from the outset.

About this time work also began on the new von Ohain S.11 engine (later known officially as the 109-011), intended to have a thrust of 1300kg (2866lb). The S.11 had a compressor with a diagonal-flow impeller stage and three axial-flow stages, an annular combustion chamber with 16 injection nozzles and an axial two-stage turbine with hollow blades. The exhaust nozzle was variable, with two positions. Contemporary reports suggest that the RLM saw the role of a new von Ohain engine as the driving force for a variable-pitch propeller, to be used on a future bomber, as eventually projected under the power plant designation 021. This was to give 3300hp at a speed of 900 km/h

(559 mph). In fact the S.11 was seen as an initial stage in the 021's development, but became the production type towards the end of the war. It appears that an enormous number of experimental and prototype S.11 engines were at one time ordered, but, after some of the second series of engines had been built, emphasis shifted to 109-011A-0 preproduction examples. By January 1945 four engines of the second series had accumulated a total of 184 hours of running.

By early 1942 Heinkel was progressing fairly well with the He 280, especially in view of Messerschmitt's inability to fly its Me 262 without the use of a piston engine in its nose. Of course this was not the fault of the airframe, but the non-availability of the Junkers Jumo 004 engine. Yet still positive steps were not being made by the RLM to progress towards He 280 production, although in 1941 six further prototypes had been ordered. A demonstration was considered the only way of really proving the He 280's ability as a fighter and so a mock dogfight was arranged between an He 280 and the best piston-engined fighter than available to the Luftwaffe, the Focke-Wulf Fw 190. In this the He 280 outflew the Fw 190; almost immediately thirteen preproduction He 280As were ordered.

The jubilation was short lived for Heinkel. As the S.8 engine was still not producing the required thrust, Heinkel reluctantly re-engined an He 280 with preproduction Junkers Jumo 004A turbojets. Therefore in July 1942 both the He 280 and Me 262 flew with 004A engines. Heavier than the S.8s, the 004As were nevertheless successful, but more so on the Me 262, as subsequent flights proved. In 1943 the S.8 engine was abandoned. Meanwhile the S.30 had been showing real promise. It first ran in October 1942 and was now the only Heinkel-Hirth engine that could be used in an early production He 280. However the RLM took a different view and ordered the S.30 to be abandoned also, in order to direct all energy to the S.11.

This decision has often been condemned by historians and indeed it did cause the premature end of a promising engine. But, seen from the RLM's point of view, the decision was not so wrong. By this time the ministry had the sound Junkers Jumo 004 as its first generation turbojet, which proved suitable for the He 280 and Me 262 prototypes, and saw the S.11 (109-011) as a follow-on type, with other engines in the pipeline.

Now that the two aircraft were flying with similar engines, the RLM could compare like with like. The Me 262 was not without its problems, but in most respects it appeared to hold greater promise. Above all, the Me 262 had a much better combat radius by virtue of its larger fuel tanks. Its cannon armament was also heavier than that originally proposed for the He 280. But still the final choice was not easy and it was complicated further when Heinkel suggested that an improved fighter-bomber version of its He 280, with more powerful Jumo 004B engines, would far outpace the 004A-engined aircraft then flying. As a fighter-bomber was close to the heart of the RLM, the proposal nearly won the day. But when further investigation showed that the Me 262 with 004B engines could prove even better, development of the He 280 was finally ordered to end in early 1943. The period of backing both 'horses' had ended. It is sometimes claimed that the personality tangle between members of the RLM and Ernst Heinkel had much to do with this decision, but it should be realized that the He 280 had other problems, including a very suspect tailplane. Therefore only the nine prototypes of the He 280 were built.

As mentioned earlier, Messerschmitt's Me 262 had to await delivery of the Jumo 004A engines before it could fly on turbojet power alone and indeed the first flight of an Me 262, on 18 April 1941, was on the power of a Junkers Jumo 210G piston engine installed in the nose. On 25 March 1942 the same aircraft, Me 262V1, took off under the power of the nose piston engine and two underwing BMW 003 turbojets, but the latter engines failed. Therefore it was not until 18 July 1942 that Me 262V3 flew with only the 004As. Well before the He 280 was abandoned officially, extra Me 262 prototypes and preproduction examples had been ordered. The latter were to use the improved 004B engine and in consequence it was not until October 1943 that the first appeared as Me 262V6.

So-called preproduction aircraft up to V12 were used in various tests, but Me 262s that were completed thereafter, up to the agreed total of 30 preproduction aircraft ordered, became true Me 262A-0s. Most of these were delivered from April 1944 to the specially-formed evaluation unit Erprobungskommando 262, which also later re-

Right: Gloster Meteor F.Mk.I jet fighters serving with No 616 Squadron RAF are pictured in 1944.

ceived the first full production Me 262A-1a fighters. It was this unit that claimed the first Allied aircraft destroyed by jet aircraft, during a series of experimental interceptions, but the unit's main role was to formulate tactics and train pilots. Interceptions of a number of reconnaissance aircraft were made, but on 25 July an RAF Mosquito survived an Me 262 attack in which the jet was lost. By then production was gradually stepping up and just over a month later P-47 Thunderbolt fighters of the USAAF's 78th Fighter Group destroyed an Me 262A-2a fighter-bomber of KG 51 Kommando Schenk, which had moved to Juvincourt on 10 July to begin operations over France with just a handful of aircraft. But why was a fighter-bomber the first Me 262 brought down by US fighters and how did the jet rate against fully-developed piston-engined fighters of 1944?

As later experience showed, the Me 262 fighter was an outstanding warplane with

Below: the Heinkel He 162A-2 Volksjäger was intended to be a mass-produced home defense fighter.

much higher performance than any piston-engined fighter. It is for this reason that historians often write that had the fighter been ready for service earlier, and in greater numbers, it could have altered the course of the war. One often quoted reason for delay in getting numbers of jet fighters into operational use was Hitler's insistence that the Me 262 should be a fighter-bomber and not merely a cannon-armed fighter. This role had been ordered by Hitler in late 1943 and reaffirmed after the Allied in-

vasion of Normandy on 6 June 1944. To say the least, Hitler was not pleased when informed that the Me 262A-0s and early production aircraft had no provision for carrying bombs. Me 262A-1a Schwalbe (Swallow) fighters on the production lines were ordered to be converted into Me 262A-2a Sturmvogel (Stormbird) fighter-bombers, with provision for two 250kg bombs or one 500kg bomb and associated equipment. It is probably true to say that Hitler had already accepted advice that

some of the Me 262s being built ought to be fighters, but, on finding that none had been built as fighter-bombers, was furious. Although wishing to advise against this course, those around Hitler retreated and for a decisive period fighter-bombers were given priority.

The modification from fighter to fighter-bomber did not hold up Me 262 production to any extent, but naturally delayed the widespread deployment of the pure jet fighter. Only in November 1944 was the emphasis on the fighter-bomber variant dropped, when all-out production of fighters was seen as the only way of curbing the crippling armadas of Allied bombers raiding Germany. Apart from lowering the Me 262's performance, because of the added weight of bombs, its adoption as a fighter-bomber was also responsible in part for a quirk of history, for no Allied jet fighter ever met a German jet in aerial combat, despite RAF Meteors being sent into Europe with the 2nd Tactical Air Force.

Whatever Hitler's policy toward the aircraft's role, the real reason for delay in getting substantial numbers of Me 262s into service was technical rather than political. Whilst airframes could be produced at a gradually increasing rate from early 1944, development of the turbojet had taken longer than expected. Indeed it was not until mid-year that the engine was considered suitably developed for mass production. Original Me 262 production schedules went out of the window, as did

later schedules that called for the production of more than 1300 by the end of 1944. For whatever reason, including Allied bombing raids on manufacturing plant, only 1433 Me 262s of all versions were built and just 200 or thereabouts became operational with the Luftwaffe. Versions of the aircraft produced, other than those already men-

Below: the de Havilland Vampire F. Mk. I was too late to see wartime service in 1945.

tioned, included the Me 262B-la tandem two-seat trainer, Me 262B-la/U1 and B-2a night fighters and the Me 262C rocket-assisted interceptor.

The Me 262 itself was powered by two 900kg (1984lb) thrust Junkers Jumo 004B eight-stage axial-flow turbojet engines in nacelles below the cantilever low and marginally-swept wings. Each engine was started by a Riedel two-stroke motor. The near triangular-section, semi-monocoque, all-metal fuselage was built in four parts and housed the four main fuel tanks with a total capacity of 2570 litres (566 Imperial gallons) of J-2 diesel oil fuel. The nose cone section incorporated four 30mm MK 108 cannon, two with 100 rounds of ammunition each and two with 80 rounds each. The pilot sat high in the cockpit under a sideways-hinged canopy, protected by 15mm armor plate and a 90mm bullet-resisting windscreen. Maximum speed for the fighter was an incredible 868 km/h (539 mph).

The controversy as to whether the Me 262 or Gloster Meteor was the first jet to enter operational service still goes on, although it is more generally accepted that the German aircraft beat the British type to this honor. It is certainly true that Erprobungskommando 262 flew Me 262s well before No 616 Squadron RAF received Meteor F.Mk Is, but this was not a fully operational unit in the accepted definition. Certainly other German units had Me 262s in July, but whether they became fully operational until August is another matter. Even General-leutnant Adolf Galland, who formed and led JV 44, has been said to have quoted August. What is known is that on 12 July 1944 No 616 Squadron received the first operational Meteors, each of which was powered by two 771kg (1700lb) thrust Rolls-Royce Welland I turbojet engines mounted within the cantilever low and tapering wings. In fact the engines were positioned near the extremities of the wing center-section, which was integral with the oval-section all-metal stressed-skin fuselage. Armament comprised four 20mm British Hispano cannon and a camera gun was installed in the nose. As with the Me 262, the pilot sat high in the cockpit, protected by armor plate and a bullet-resisting windscreen.

Britain had pulled out all the stops in getting the Meteor into service so quickly, especially bearing in mind that the Gloster E.28/39 had not flown by the time Heinkel was flying its He 280 prototype fighter. Helped by the use of eight F. 9/40 proto-types, with which to test various British engines, the development of the actual fighter was rapid. The first F.9/40 prototype flew for the first time on 5 March 1943 with Halford H.1 (Goblin) engines fitted, followed by the W2B-engined F.9/40 in June of that year. The Metropolitan-Vickers F.2/1-engined F.9/40 flew on 13 November 1943 (to become the first prototype flying with axial-flow turbojet engines), while the most unusual was undoubtedly the Rolls-Royce Trent-engined aircraft.

Meteor F.Mk Is were declared operational on 27 July and on that day began operations against V-1 flying-bombs, which had been directed at Britain since 13 June. An attempt to shoot down a V-1 on that day proved abortive, but on 4 August one was destroyed when the pilot of a Meteor flew alongside the missile and tipped it over with his aircraft's wing. On the same day another V-1 was brought down by cannon fire. The Meteor had arrived, albeit flying at only 676 km/h (420 mph).

Only twenty Meteor F.Mk Is were produced, most of which flew with No 616 Squadron. Of the remaining four, three were used as development aircraft and one was sent to America in exchange for a US-built Bell P-59 Airacomet. Other wartime Meteor variants included the prototype F.Mk 2 (with Goblin engines) and the F.Mk 3. The latter was the first major production version of the Meteor, of which all but 15 of the 280 built were powered by Derwent I engines. The F.Mk 3 had provision for a fuselage drop-tank to increase range. Maximum speed of this version was 793 km/h (493 mph). Later versions of the Meteor are covered in the next chapter.

Another British jet fighter which was built and flown during World War II was the de Havilland DH.100 Vampire. This was very different from the Meteor in that it was designed to use only one Goblin turbojet engine. Because of this, and in order not to lose any of the available 1225kg (2700lb) of thrust, the engine was placed in a short fuselage nacelle aft of the pilot's cockpit, which did away with the need for a long air intake and long jetpipe. This installation necessitated a twin-boom tail unit. In fact the fuselage nose was basically that from the company's highly-successful Mosquito and was, therefore, of plywood-balsa-plywood sandwich construction. The straight but tapering wings were all-metal and incorporated the engine air intakes in the roots. The prototype Vampire flew for the first time on 20 September 1943 and the first production aircraft flew on 20 April 1945. However Vampires did not enter service with the RAF until 1946.

Above: an American Bell P-59 Airacomet was exchanged for a British Gloster Meteor in 1943.

A single-engined jet fighter was also built in Germany, but under very different circumstances. By September 1944 the most Germany could hope to do was to defend itself against Allied forces closing in on all fronts. At the beginning of that month it was decided that, despite the production of the excellent Me 262, a new jet fighter was needed that could be produced quickly and in very great numbers to intercept Allied bombers that were destroying German factories and communications. This new fighter could be spared one engine only (a BMW 003), it had to be constructed of materials then available, it had to conform to strict weight and take off distance limitations but still achieve at least 750 km/h (466 mph), and could be armed with one or two 30mm cannon. Equally important was that it had to be simple enough to be built by

semi-skilled workers overseeing the un-skilled, thus making use of forced and voluntary labor.

Less than a week was allowed for initial proposals and several companies submitted designs. Messerschmitt wanted nothing to do with such a scheme, which appeared to encroach upon its own Me 262, but Heinkel was anxious to submit a design, having been banned from further work on jet aircraft after its He 280 episode. In fact Heinkel had already worked on the idea of a 'lightweight' fighter, as the Spatz (Sparrow), and this formed the basis of the new Project 1073, which eventually became the He 162 Salamander.

Bearing in mind the necessity to keep the fighter simple, Heinkel decided to adopt the V-1 flying-bomb approach to power plant and placed the single engine on the top of the fuselage, exhausting through a V-tail. For the RLM, only two designs appeared to be worth pursuing seriously, those of Blohm und Voss and Heinkel, with a

strong bias for the former. But Heinkel kept up the pressure, pointing out that it had progressed further with development and was therefore in a better position to meet the tight schedules.

On 23 September the decision was made to go ahead with the concept of a Volks-jäger (People's Fighter) and the Heinkel proposal was selected, a decision helped by the display of a mock-up which had been completed by 20 September. The idea of a Volksjäger reflected Hitler's own thinking for the setting up of a vast Home Guard-type force to protect the homeland against the advancing Allies, with members of the Hitler Youth and old men making up shortages in numbers. Independently Goering envisioned thousands of members of the Hitler Youth being trained to fly on gliders, the most promising then progressing on to the Volksjäger with little or no intermediate powered flight training. This vast intake of new pilots would match the massive production of jet fighters at conventional plant

and in the underground salt and potassium mine factories. Heinkel pulled out all the stops in order to meet schedules, but at least Ernst Heinkel knew full well that the whole concept of boy pilots was a pipedream and at best would provide only a respite from the inevitable defeat of Germany.

On 29 September Heinkel received the contract and on 6 December the prototype He 162 flew for the first time at Vienna-Schwechat, completing 20 minutes in the air. the elapsed time between contract and first flight had been just 69 days, 90 from the conception of the Volksjäger by the RLM. On 10 December a second flight ended in disaster, when the He 162 crashed after losing the leading-edge and tip of one wing and an aileron. The Volksjäger had claimed its first victim.

On examination it became clear that the design of the wooden wings with straight leading-edges and detachable metal tips was not the cause of the accident, but that the bonding used had caused some deterioration of the wood: the stress of a high speed dash had been too great for the deteriorated structure. However this is not to say that the He 162 was otherwise pleasant to fly. Far from it, as it proved relatively unstable because of the position of the engine and required careful use of the controls. It is interesting to note that the once-favored Blohm und Voss design had the engine more sensibly mounted inside the fuselage, exhausting below a 'boom' tail to avoid the loss of power which a long jetpipe would entail.

Although the Volksjäger was to be flown by pilots not already in the Luftwaffe, a Luftwaffe evaluation unit was set up to take the first production He 162s. Similarly it was later decided expedient to allow experienced Luftwaffe pilots to crew the first operational aircraft. But Heinkel's impressive start in keeping to schedules could not be sustained and, whilst 50 production He 162s were ordered for January 1945, followed by 100 for February, and then quickly building up to 1,000 per month, only a handful of production aircraft were available by the end of January. In the following month He 162s produced included prototypes for improved models.

Utter confusion followed, as production factories had to close with the Allied advance, including in April those in Vienna which had made use of voluntary non-German workers, while Luftwaffe units were moved from one airfield to another. On 3 May a number of He 162s were among the aircraft left behind by the retreating Germans at Salzburg, although they had been destroyed. On the following day I Einsatz-Gruppe JG 1 formed at Leck, mustering about fifty He 162s. This was the only He 162-equipped group at the end of the war and during its four days at Leck it only managed a minimum of flying, mainly because of fuel shortages. On 8 May the group surrendered to the Allies. So ended Goering's grand Volksjäger plan. It is believed that between 250 and 300 He 162s had been built by the time of the German capitulation, with hundreds more nearing completion. Of these the Luftwaffe received 116, but the fighter was rarely seen in the air by Allied aircrews. Nevertheless Heinkel had achieved the near impossible with the He 162, which could fly at 840 km/h (522 mph) on the power of its single BMW 003E

Right: two Bell YP-59A Airacomet service test aircraft fly in echelon formation.

Above: Japan's only wartime jet fighter was the Nakajima Kikka, seen displayed in a museum.

engine, could climb to 6000m (19,685ft) in a little over 6.5 minutes, and was armed with two 20mm MG 151 cannon with 120 rounds of ammunition per gun.

Across the Atlantic the jet fighter was also in its infancy. In September 1941 the Bell Aircraft Corporation was requested to design a jet fighter using the British Whittle-type engine, an early example of which was received by General Electric. A preliminary design was submitted in October the same year, which was approved. The aircraft was given the USAAF designation XP-59A, which was devised to maintain strict secrecy, as it implied a variant of the experimental XP-59 pusher-engined (piston) and twin-boom fighter. The XP-59A

was designed very much on the lines of Bell's P-39 Airacobra/P-63A Kingcobra piston-engined fighters, apart from the power plant and mid-wings. Of all-metal construction, the XP-59A, named Aira-comet, was a single-seater armed with one 37mm cannon and three 0.50in machine-guns in its extreme nose. Bomb racks were positioned under each wing. The two General Electric Type 1-A engines were mounted in nacelles beneath the wing roots, exhausting to the rear of the wing trailing-edges. This arrangement kept the air intakes and jetpipes to short lengths.

The detail design of the XP-59A took about six months, when work on component parts began. In September 1942 the first prototype was shipped to the secret aircraft flight testing base at Muroc in California, where the engines were started for the first time. On the last day of September the XP-59A undertook taxiing trials, and the next

day made its first flight lasting half an hour. On 2 October two very successful flights were made, one reaching an altitude of 3050m (10,000ft). In total three prototypes were built.

Thirteen service evaluation YP-59As followed, these being delivered in 1943. Actual production began with twenty P-59As with 750kg (1650lb) thrust General Electric I-16 or J31-GE-3 turbojet engines, followed by thirty P-59Bs with 907kg (2000lb) thrust J31-GE-5 engines, which entered USAAF service from August 1944. These were the only production examples of the Airacomet built and were used mainly as jet fighter trainers. The P-59B had a maximum speed of 665 km/h (413 mph), less than that being achieved by the highly-developed piston-engined fighters then in service and the prototypes of the Fisher P-75A Eagle type then flying.

Far more important to the postwar USAF

was the jet fighter under development at Lockheed, which in first prototype form used British-designed engines. In June 1943 Lockheed was requested to design and build a new single-seat fighter, using a British de Havilland H.1 turbojet as the power plant, which arrived in America in the following month and was delivered to Wright Field. The first prototype was to be completed in just 180 days as the XP-80 Shooting Star, but Lockheed bettered this by having it airborne within 143 days, on 8 January 1944.

Unlike the other American jet, the British Meteor and the German Me 262, the XP-80 had its engine installed in the fuselage center-section. Air intakes were positioned in the fuselage sides, just forward of the wing roots. Already two other prototypes and 13 service evaluation aircraft had been ordered, but these had to be modified considerably when the Allis-Chalmers

Company was unable to mass produce the H.1 in America. In consequence it was not until mid-1944 that the next XP-80A prototype could fly, incorporating a more-powerful 1700kg (3750lb) thrust General Electric I-40 engine, which meant a longer fuselage, greater wing span, a redesigned vertical tail and a modified and strengthened landing gear.

The thirteen YP-80As were powered by General-Electric J33-GE-9 or -11 engines and had six 0.50in machine guns instead of the previous five. The YP-80As were delivered to the USAAF from October 1944 and two were despatched to Europe. The first true production model was the P-80A, deliveries to the USAAF beginning in December 1945 and therefore P-80As not becoming active during World War II. Previously Lockheed had made preparations for P-80A construction at four plants and the North American Kansas City plant

was also to be included. With the end of the war in Europe cutbacks were made and the North American contract was terminated.

Japan's jet-powered fighter, known as the Nakajima Kikka and flown only twice in prototype form during the last few days of war (for a total of only a few minutes), was based on the German Me 262. It was powered by two 475kg (1047lb) thrust Ne-20 axial-flow turbojet engines. Had the war continued into 1946, there can be little doubt that Japanese and American jet fighters would have met, as other prototype and preproduction Kikka jets were in the process of being built. Similarly British and German jets would have fought each other in the skies of Europe. But one thing was certain in 1945, the early jet fighters had such advantages over well-developed piston-engined warplanes that there could be no turning back and no postwar slump in aircraft production.

3: FAREWELL THE PISTON

With the defeat of Germany the Allies began collecting up the tons of documents relating to advanced military projects, a large proportion of which related to aviation. Plenty of prototype and production aircraft with little or no damage could also be examined, many finding their way into other countries. It soon became clear that Germany had already begun considering aircraft with delta, fully swept and variable-geometry wings, together with

Above: the S-92 fighter was a Messerschmitt Me 262 built in Czechoslovakia after World War II.

advanced propulsion systems such as ramjets.

Because of the very advanced nature of some German research, it is often overlooked that Britain had overcome its pathetically slow start in developing turbojet-powered aircraft, finishing the war with sound airframes and excellent turbojet engines. It is true that British jets of the war period were not the fastest, but they held plenty of promise for development. As a victor, Britain was able to continue work on its Meteor and Vampire, whilst the Me 262 and He 162 died. However the Me 262 was reprieved temporarily, when a small number were completed in Czechoslovakia as S-92 fighters and CS-92 fighter-bombers.

Below: the Gloster Meteor F. Mk. 8 was the major production version of Britain's first jet fighter.

The last 15 Gloster Meteor F.Mk 3s built had longer nacelles around the Derwent engines. This feature, together with Derwent 5 engines, reduced wing span to increase the aircraft's rate of roll, a pressurised cabin for the pilot and the provision for carrying bombs and rockets, became standard on the postwar Meteor F.Mk 4. The first F.Mk 4 flew in April 1945 and on 7 November that year an example set up the first official world speed record for aircraft since early 1939, achieving 975.67 km/h (606.25 mph) at Herne Bay, Kent. Over the next few years other fighter, fighter-reconnaissance, two-seat training, two-seat night fighter (the NF.Mk 11 becoming the RAF's first jet night fighter in 1951) and unarmed

Overleaf: the Lockheed T-33A was the training variant of the P-80 Shooting Star and saw widespread service.

high-altitude reconnaissance variants of the Meteor were produced, the F.Mk 8 fighter becoming the major production version. This was a longer-range development of the F.Mk 4, featuring a redesigned cockpit which included a pilot ejection seat. The latter, which ultimately saved the lives of many pilots, had been first tested in an earlier Meteor on 24 July 1946, when the first 'live' ejection was made at a speed of 515 km/h (320 mph). In total approximately 3550 Meteors of all versions were built in Britain, nearly one-third as F.Mk 8s. Eleven other countries eventually acquired Meteors. During the Korean War, the F.Mk 8 was the only British-designed jet fighter to be flown operationally, serving with the RAAF.

The other British wartime jet, the Vampire, was somewhat overshadowed by the Meteor, but it nevertheless has the distinction of remaining in service with one or two air forces in the early 1980s. The prototype Vampire exceeded 805 km/h (500 mph) in the spring of 1944 and in this respect bettered the Meteor and the Bell Airacomet.

The F.Mk 1 entered production soon after, with an order for 120 sub-contracted to the English Electric Company. Goblin 1 engines powered the first forty production aircraft, superseded by the 1406kg (3100lb) thrust Goblin 2. The first 50 had three-piece canopies and used drop tanks to increase range, but subsequent fighters featured pressurized cockpits with bubble canopies and had larger fuel tanks in the wings.

No 247 Squadron RAF became the first to operate the Vampire in mid-1946, soon joined by other regular and auxiliary squadrons. A de Havilland Ghost-powered Vampire and the experimental Vampire Mk 2s with Rolls-Royce Nene 1 engines were fol-

lowed by the Goblin 2 engined Vampire F.Mk 3, a long-range fighter with increased fuel tankage and redesigned tail unit. The first F.Mk 3 flew on 4 November 1946. Six F.Mk 3s became the first RAF turbojet-powered aircraft to cross the North Atlantic in 1948.

In addition to RAF production, Vampire F.Mk 1s and F.Mk 3s were exported, the fighters having been ordered by Sweden, Switzerland, Norway and Canada. The Mk 4, the intended production version of the Mk 2, did not enter production in Britain, but was built under licence in Australia with Mk 30 series designations. Subsequent overseas versions included the FB.Mk 6 fighter-bomber powered by the 1500kg (3300lb) thrust Goblin 3 exported to, and built in, Switzerland, the similar Swedish FB.Mk 50, Norwegian FB.Mk 52 and the French FB.Mk 53. The latter is of particular interest as it was based on the FB.Mk 5 but entered production in France as the SNCASE Mistral. Powered by an Hispano-Suiza-built Nene engine, it was built entirely of French materials and followed French production of the FB.Mk 5. The first SNCASE-produced Vampire FB.Mk 5 flew on 27 January 1950 and SNCASE built 430 Vampire and Mistral aircraft in total.

The FB.Mk 5 itself was produced as a ground attack fighter for the RAF, using the Goblin 2 engine. Wing span was reduced from 12.19m (40ft) to 11.58m (38ft) and other changes included strengthened wings to allow for the provision of eight rockets and two 500lb bombs, two 1000lb bombs or two drop tanks. The first FB.Mk 5 flew in June

Left: this Shooting Star was one of a number of P-80As converted to carry cameras in the nose as FP-80As.

Below: the British D.H. Vampire was built under license in France as the SNCASE Mistral.

1948 and superseded the F.Mk 3, operating in Britain, Germany and the Middle and Far East. A special version of the FB.Mk 5 was produced for RAF squadrons operating in tropical climates as the FB.Mk 9. Other Vampires to enter production included two-seat trainers, the D.H.113 night fighter (95 two-seaters were flown by the RAF as NF.Mk 10s between 1951 and 1954) and the Sea Vampire. The prototype Sea Vampire was in fact a converted RAF fighter with an arrester hook and larger-area dive-brakes and landing flaps. On 3 December 1945 it landed and took off again from HMS *Ocean*, the first time a turbojet-powered aircraft performed this. The Navy received a small number of production Sea Vampires as F.Mk 20s, incorporating FB.Mk 5-type wings, although strengthened, and armed with the usual four 20mm British Hispano cannon. Including the very large number of trainers built, well over 2000 Vampires left production lines in Britain.

Between the end of the war and June 1947 the British Meteor F.Mk 4 held on to the world speed record for aeroplanes, increasing the record over that period. Then on 19 June a Lockheed Shooting Star achieved 1003.6 km/h (623.61 mph) at Muroc, California, bettering an unofficial Meteor speed set in September 1946 by a fraction of a second. This marked not only the beginning of America's dominance of the record, until the introduction of the British Hunter fighter, but the growing importance of the Shooting Star in USAAF service.

The P-80A went into service from December 1945, powered by one Allison

J33-A-9, -11 or -17 engine. Although it had been planned to produce 5000 of these fighters, postwar cancellations meant that only just over ten percent was actually built. These subsequently became F-80As under the new designation system. By March 1948 F-80As had ben modified to include water/alcohol injection, cockpit cooling, underwing rocket launchers and provision for JATO, features designed into the P-80B/F-80B, which also had a thinner wing, strengthened bulkheads in the nose, enclosed radio mast and antennae wires and a 2360kg (5200lb) thrust Allison J33-A-21 engine. Altogether 240 'Bs' were produced.

The final production version of the Shooting Star single-seat fighter was the P-80C/F-80C, powered by the 2360kg (5200lb) thrust J33-A-23 or 2450kg (5400lb) thrust J33-A-35 engine. Armament was improved by the use of six updated and faster-firing M-3 0.50in guns, as well as by the provision for carrying two 1000lb bombs or rockets. As with earlier versions, the guns and ammunition magazines could be replaced in

fifteen minutes. A total of 798 P-80C/F-80Cs was built, one of which made history by shooting down a Chinese-flown Mikoyan-Gurevich MiG-15 over Korea on 8 November 1950, the first recorded victory of one jet fighter over another in combat. During this war the Shooting Star was operated mainly in a ground atack role. Thousands of sorties by Shooting Stars were made over Korea, although as a fighter it had to bow to the superior swept-wing North American F-86 Sabre. Non-combat versions of the Shooting Star included the RF-80C photographic reconnaissance aircraft, the T-33A two-seat trainer and the US Navy TO-1 and TO-2 (later TV-1 and 2) single and two-seat trainers and the T2V Seastar Navy trainer. It is worth noting that the T-33A became the most produced version, with well over 5000 being built.

Another combat aircraft, related to the T-33A, was the Lockheed F-94A Starfire. Powered by the Allison J33-A-33 turbojet, it was evolved as an all-weather fighter, with radar equipment in the nose. A radar

operator occupied the rear tandem seat. Armed with four 0.50in guns, it used the wings, center fuselage and other components of the T-33A. One hundred and ten F-94As were produced, entering service with the USAF in mid-1950. The F-94A was followed by the refined F-94B, of which 357 were built. The most noticeable external change was its new wingtip tanks, positioned at the tips (not underneath as on the F-94A).

The final production version of the Starfire was the F-94C, powered by the 3765kg (8300lb) thrust Pratt & whitney J48-P-5 engine and incorporating a longer forward fuselage, thinner wings, new and swept horizontal tail surfaces, a larger fin and rudder and new main armament of 24 Mighty Mouse air-to-air rockets carried around the radome at the nose and covered by a circular retractable fairing. A similar number of rockets could be carried in a further two pods mounted on the wing leading edges. Production of the F-94C amounted to 387 aircraft.

When the Starfire entered service it became the USAF's first all-weather interceptor, beating the Northrop Scorpion, serving mainly with Air Defense Command. A single-seat tactical fighter version of the F-94C was proposed as the F-94D, for operation in Korea, but this idea went no further. It is interesting to note that despite its much heavier take-off weight, the F-94C's speed of 941 km/h (585 mph) was slightly higher than that of the F-80C.

Three other straight-winged American jet fighters appeared in production form soon after the end of World War II, namely the McDonnell FD-1 Phantom, the Republic F-84 Thunderjet and the Northrop F-89 Scorpion. The Phantom was in fact a naval fighter that had the distinction of being the first US fighter with turbojet power only to land on an aircraft carrier.

The Republic F-84 Thunderjet was the first of the other two to enter production for the USAAF, having flown in prototype form on 28 February 1946. As originally conceived, it was not only intended as a re-

placement for the piston-engined Republic P-47 Thunderbolt, but to be basically a redesign of it to take a General Electric TG-180 (J35) axial-flow turbojet engine. However in late 1944 this proposal was discarded in favor of producing a completely new airframe.

The Thunderjet became an all-metal aircraft with a circular-section fuselage of greatly varying diameter. The engine was placed inside the fuselage to the rear of the wings, the fuselage itself reducing in diameter towards the nose air intake and tail jetpipe. Because the rear section of the fuselage was detachable, the engine could be replaced in under an hour. Fuel tanks were in the wings, while jettisonable tiptanks allowed for increased range. Armament comprised six 0.50in guns (four in the nose and two in the wings). From the 86th aircraft armament was increased by the use of retractable launchers beneath the wings for eight 5 inch rockets, although previous F-84Bs could carry rockets beneath the wings.

Above left: the Republic F-84E Thunderjet was operated as a fighter-bomber by the USAF.

Above: the Lockheed F-94C Starfire carried 24 Mighty Mouse rockets around the nose radome.

In September 1946 the second prototype Thunderjet attained a speed of 983 km/h (611 mph), thus setting a new American speed record. The usual batch of pre-production aircraft, in this case designated YF-84As and powered by 1814kg (4000lb) thrust Allison J35-A-15 engines, was followed by the full production F-84B (originally P-84B), deliveries of which began in 1947 to the 14th Fighter Group. The 'B' was powered by the similarly-rated J35-A-15C and the preproduction aircraft were brought up to this standard.

The F-84C was basically a slightly refined version of the 'B,' but the follow-on F-84D introduced many changes. Apart from being powered by the 2268kg (5000lb)

Above: an underside view of the Republic F-84F Thunderstreak prototype aircraft.

thrust Allison J35-A-17D turbojet, with a winterized fuel system using gasoline, it used thicker metal skins on the wings and ailerons, had a shorter landing gear with mechanical linkages and other changes. This version was the first to be flown in Korea, becoming active from the end of 1950.

From the F-84D was developed the F-84E, which had a longer fuselage to permit more room in the cockpit (increasing pilot comfort and efficiency); wingtip tanks fitted with fins to provide better maneuverability with the tanks attached (making it unnecessary to jettison the tanks before combat); structural changes to permit higher G forces; use of a radar gunsight; addition of two 230 US gallon (871 liter) drop tanks that could be carried by the inboard bomb shackles to increase the aircraft's radius of combat to more than 1609km (1000 miles), from the normal 1127km (700 miles) or thereabouts; provision for JATO (jet assisted take off) and other improvements. Armament also received attention, allowing for the carriage of 32 5in rockets (24 under the outer wings and eight on inboard stations), or two 1000lb bombs and 18 rockets. This armament indicated the Thunderjet's increasing importance as a fighter-bomber.

The F-84F was not the next version of the Thunderjet, but a more modern development of it named Thunderstreak. It was basically a swept-wing F-84E, powered by a 3275kg (7220lb) thrust Armstrong Siddeley Sapphire ASSa 3 turbojet engine which was being produced in the United States under license by the Wright Aeronautical Corporation. Interestingly the Sapphire was a development of the original Metropolitan Vickers engine. The prototype Thunderstreak, powered by an Allison J35-A-25 engine, took off for the first time on 3 June 1950 as the YF-96A, but the second prototype flew on 14 February 1951 with the Sapphire engine as the XF-84F. The production F-84F became operational with the USAF in 1954, but approximately half of the 2711 aircraft built were acquired by other NATO air forces. Maximum level speed of the F-84F was 1058 km/h (658 mph), compared to the F-84E's 986 km/h (613 mph). A tactical reconnaissance version of the Thunderstreak was the RF-84F Thunderflash, which could be identified easily by the fairing-over of the nose air intake (replaced by intakes in the wing roots) to provide accommodation for the cameras, radar and other electronic equipment. By the end of 1956 a total of 715 Thunderflash reconnaissance aircraft had been built.

Like the later Thunderstreak, F-84E Thunderjets were also acquired by other NATO air forces. However by far the most important version of the Thunderjet was the F-84G, which became the first fighter-bomber operated by the USAF to be capable of carrying and delivering an atomic bomb. It was powered by the 2540kg (5600lb) thrust Allison J35-A-29 turbojet engine, was capable of inflight refuelling using the 'flying boom' method, had an automatic pilot fitted and proved to be the

Above: the F-84G Thunderjet was supplied to many NATO air forces, including that of Turkey.

Left: a pair of Northrop F-89 Scorpion all-weather interceptor fighters fly in formation during 1956.

fastest version of the Thunderjet with a maximum level speed of 1001 km/h (622 mph). Of the 4457 Thunderjets of all versions built, the 'G' amounted to 3025, deliveries to other NATO air forces and others eligible under MAP (Military Assistance Program) accounting for 1936.

The Northrop F-89 Scorpion was evolved as a two-seat, all-weather jet interceptor fighter and in this respect was similar to the Lockheed Starfire. However although its development had begun as early as 1946, it followed the Starfire into USAF service, not becoming operational until 1951. The XF-89 prototype first flew on 16 August 1948 and during the course of its test program the ailerons were replaced by 'decelerons,' new power-operated ailerons which were split to serve as both ailerons and dive brakes. As dive brakes, the upper and lower segments could be extended up and down simultaneously. Power was provided by two 1814kg (4000lb) thrust Allison J35-A-9 engines, mounted one each side of the fuselage under the wings, partly submerged into the fuselage contours.

The second prototype was powered by

2222kg (4900lb) thrust J35-A-21 engines with afterburners and was followed by the first 18 production Scorpions designated F-89As. Armament comprised six 20mm cannon in the nose and the J35-A-21 engines were later replaced by more powerful J35-A-21As. The second production version was also produced in small numbers, differing little from the F-89A. The first major production version was the F-89C, which was fitted during its production run with several different engines up to the J35-A-33A. Like previous Scorpions, it too had wingtip fuel tanks (fitted with horizontal fins) and could supplement its gun armament with bombs and a small number of rockets. Its main innovation was the use of new internally-balanced elevators, which were subsequently fitted to earlier aircraft in place of the previously-used external mass balances.

Of the 1050 Scorpions built, more than 680 were F-89Ds. The majority were powered by 2540kg (5600lb) thrust J35-A-35 engines. The 'D' was the first and only version of the Scorpion to use the newly-developed wingtip pods, each containing fuel and 52 2.75in folding-fin air-to-air rockets, the gun armament being deleted. Rockets could be fired in batches of seven or in a volley from behind fairings. Other important changes included the use of two jettisonable underwing pylon-mounted auxiliary fuel tanks for extended range.

The experimental XF-89E (Allison J71 engines), F-89F and F-89G remained prototypes and projects, leaving the F-89H as the follow-on to the F-89D. In this version new wingtip pods each carried 21 rockets and three Hughes Falcon air-to-air missiles, the latter emerging from the pods before firing. Underwing pylons allowed a further batch of Falcon missiles to be carried. F-89Hs became operational in 1956, three years after the 'D,' but served for only a very short time with Air Defense Command. However a further version of the Scorpion appeared as the F-89J, basically an F-89D modified to carry two Douglas MB-1 Genie air-to-air missiles with nuclear warheads, as well as four Falcon missiles and rockets.

In Europe both France and Sweden got off to an early start by producing jet fighters in the 1940s. Sweden had been among the few countries experimenting with a turbojet engine prior to the outbreak of World War II and on 10 March 1947 Saab flew a version of its Model 21A pusher-engined fighter with the DB 605B piston engine replaced by a Goblin turbojet. In this configuration the aircraft became the Saab-21R. The Flygvap-

net (Swedish air force) received sixty aircraft from 1950, powered by Goblin 2 and SFA-built Goblin 3 engines with the military designations J21RA and J21RB respectively. As a fighter the Saab-21R was armed with one 20mm cannon and two 13mm Bofors guns in the nose and two guns in the wings, as was standard for the piston-engined version. A pack containing eight guns could also be carried under the fuselage nacelle. However because of the rapid development of the purpose-designed Saab-29, the Saab-21R soon found itself transferred to a ground attack role as the A 21R.

The Saab-29 was the first purpose-designed Swedish jet fighter, originally intended to have straight wings but later revised to become in production form the first European fully swept-wing fighter. The Saab-29 joined the F13 day fighter wing of the Flygvapnet at Norrköping in 1951. Three prototypes were ordered, the first of which flew initially on 1 September 1948 on the power of a de Havilland Ghost engine, rated at 1996kg (4400lb) thrust. Because of its unique shape, the aircraft soon received the popular name Tunnan (barrel). All production Saab-29s were powered by SFA

license-built Ghost 50 engines, known to the air force as the RM2 and rated at 2268kg (5000lb) thrust. The final version (military designation J 29F) used a Swedish-developed afterburner to raise thrust to 2800kg (6170lb), in this form the engine receiving the revised designation RM2B. The Ghost was installed inside a dumpy fuselage and exhausted beneath the tail unit. Such was the size of the fuselage, it was able to house the short landing gear when retracted, the fuel tanks, the four 20mm cannon armament and other equipment.

The initial production version of the Saab-29 was the J 29A, deliveries starting in May 1951. Initially the air brakes were wing mounted, but these later gave way to others on the fuselage. In 1953 the 'A' was superseded on the production lines by the J 29B, which had greater range by virtue of increased fuel capacity. An attack version of this model also appeared as the A 29B. The 'C' designation applied only to the S 29C photographic reconnaissance aircraft, also delivered in 1953, which carried six fully-automatic cameras.

In March 1954 the J 29D flew, but it remained an experimental version, being used to flight test the afterburner developed by SFA and the Swedish Air Board. Meanwhile in December 1953 a new outer wing had been flight tested which had been designed to increase maximum speed and improve the aircraft's flying characteristics at transonic speed. This was incorporated into production aircraft the following year, thus producing the J 29E fighter.

The final production versions of the Saab-29 were the J 29F fighter and A 29F attack aircraft, which were basically 'Es' fitted with the newly-developed afterburner. The pre-production J 29F had been flown in the first half of 1954 and deliveries of production aircraft were made between late 1954 and April 1956. The 'F' attained a maximum level speed of 1060 km/h (659 mph). In total 661 Saab-29s were built, and although several hundred earlier models were thereafter gradually brought up to 'F' standard, by 1956 Saab had already begun delivery of its latest Model 32 Lansen, and had flown a research aircraft (known as the Saab-210 Draken) which helped to develop the Saab-35 Draken fighter.

Because of the German occupation during the first half of the 1940s, France took longer to get a jet fighter into service than would otherwise have been the case. Nevertheless, its first production jet fighter, the Dassault M.D.450 Ouragan (Hurricane), was designed and constructed in a very short time. Despite the occupation, work on a turbojet-powered aircraft began as early as 1943. Although it was possible to carry out theoretical and design work in secrecy, actual construction of an airframe could not begin until after liberation. It was therefore in 1945 that the construction of five prototype Sud-Ouest SO 6000 Triton experimental two-seat jet trainers was ordered, the first to be powered by one German Junkers Jumo 004B turbojet and the rest by Hispano-Suiza-built Nene 101 engines. On 11 November 1946 the Jumo-powered SO 6000 took to the air for the first time. France had joined the exclusive few countries flying jets. A Nene-powered SO 6000 followed on 19 March 1948.

While France waited for its own aircraft industry to produce a jet fighter, it filled the time-gap by accepting British Vampires into service. The problem France might have experienced in developing rapidly its own turbojet engine was also removed by the production of the Nene engine by

Left: an F-89D Scorpion fires its wingtip rockets. A total of 104 air-to-air rockets was carried.

Above: the Saab-21R jet fighter was a development of the earlier Model 21A piston-engined aircraft.

Hispano-Suiza. It was around this engine that a specification was issued and in December 1947 Avions Marcel Dassault began work on what became the Ouragan. An official order was given for three prototypes on 1 July 1948, by which time construction at the Dassault plant had already begun. The first prototype made its maiden flight on 29 February 1949.

The Ouragan itself was a fine design, using low-mounted wings with symmetrical laminar-flow section. Leading-edges were swept at 20 degrees and trailing-edges were straight. The circular-section fuselage was built in three sections, the nose section containing the frontal air intake, pilot's cockpit and nose wheel, the center section carried the engine, fuel tanks and radio equipment; the engine exhausting at the tail. Fuel tanks were also carried in the wings,

outboard of the landing gear, while wingtip tanks allowed extended range. Armament comprised four 20mm cannon, plus optionally 16 rockets carried under the wings. Naturally, the Ouragan was the first French jet fitted with an ejection seat, produced by Martin-Baker.

Trials with the prototype Ouragans were so successful that no time was lost in ordering preproduction fighters, the first of which flew in November 1950. Full production then went ahead and in December 1951 the initial Ouragans for the French air force flew. Altogether the air force received 350, production of 30 each month being achieved by the beginning of 1953. About one-third of the production was sub-contracted to SNCASO and SNCASE. The Ouragan was also exported to India (renamed Toofani) and Israel, although most of the eventual Israeli

total of more than 50 were ex-French air force fighters. Maximum level speed of the Ouragan was 940 km/h (584 mph).

It is not overstating the case to say that British-developed turbojet engines were fundamental in getting most of the world's earliest jet fighters into the air. America had used British engines during World War II for its Bell Airacomet and Lockheed Shooting Star prototypes and after the war, France and Sweden had used British turbojets. Other nations were to follow this lead. Likewise it was only after Britain had delivered 25 Rolls-Royce Nene and 30 Derwent engines to the Soviet Union in 1947 that Soviet jet fighter design really took off in a big way. Many have since stated that this one act gave the Soviet Union such a boost that it was responsible for undermining the lead built up in the West, allowing that nation to bypass lengthy development of its own engines, or those captured from the Germans. Although there can be little doubt that the Rolls-Royce engines were of great value in this respect, the Soviet Union had managed to get a small number of very respectable jet fighters into service on the power of German-type engines alone. Also the great importance attached to the development of jet fighters by the Soviet Union in 1945 would have ensured rapid development with or without outside help.

During World War II the Soviet Union had had to put the bulk of its energy into the production of conventional weapons with which to drive German forces from its land. Often updates and modifications to improve aircraft were introduced without break in production and it was partly because of this that the only non-conventional form of pro-

pulsion used on aircraft was the rocket motor. Even then it was seen as a 'booster' and not as the main form of power as used by the Germans towards the end of the war.

The Soviet Union saw the need for both twin-jet and single-engined fighters to replace wartime piston aircraft and therefore issued two initial specifications. Interestingly the two most successful jet fighters, one single-engined and the other twin, both flew for the first time on the same day. For the twin-engined competition, Mikoyan-Gurevich produced its I-300, an impressive aircraft with straight wings. The circular-section fuselage had a divided nose air intake, which fed two developed 800kg (1764lb) thrust German BMW 003A turbojet engines mounted side by side in the rear fuselage and exhausting under the tail. This flew for the first time on 24 April 1946. In

competition was a Sukhoi jet, first flown in August that year. This used two Junkers Jumo 004B engines in pods under the wings and looked remarkably like a straight-winged Messerschmitt Me 262. The Sukhoi was not well received and indeed had a maximum speed very similar to the wartime Me 262. It was the I-300 that was selected for production as the MiG-9, its designers receiving a Stalin Prize.

The production MiG-9 used two RD-20 turbojet engines, the Soviet development and production model of the BMW, and armament comprised one 37mm Nudelmann N-37 cannon projecting from the nose and two 23mm NS-23 cannon under the

Below: the final version of the Saab J 29 Tunnan was the J 29F, which used afterburning.

Left: the Yak-23 served in small numbers with Soviet satellite air forces, a Polish fighter is shown.

nose. With a maximum speed of 910 km/h (565 mph), the MiG-9 entered service with the air force, but was not its first jet fighter. It remained operational until the early 1950s, when the fighter received the NATO reporting name *Fargo*. In addition to being based in the Soviet Union, a number were to be found in East Germany. Developments included a version with RD-21 engines.

For the single-engined jet fighter competition Lavochkin produced its La-150 and Yakovlev an adaption of the piston-engined Yak-3 which later became the Yak-15. As with all of the first Soviet jet fighter prototypes except for the Sukhoi, the La-150 used an engine which exhausted under the rear fuselage and tail. Power was provided by the RD-10, the Soviet developed version of

the German Junkers Jumo 004B. Although more work had probably gone into the development of this prototype than the Yak-15, the Lavochkin was not selected. However in 1947 Lavochkin produced its La-160, the first Soviet jet fighter prototype with swept wings. It was followed by the La-168, which subsequently lost a competition against the MiG-15 as a second-generation fighter, and the La-174, which in 1949 joined the air force in limited numbers as a fighter-bomber, powered by a development of the Rolls-Royce Derwent engine (known as the RD-500). Capable of more than 1000 km/h (620 mph), the La-174 received the military designation La-15 in production form and the reporting name *Fantail* by NATO.

The winner of the lightweight jet fighter competition, the Yak-15, first flew in prototype form on 24 April 1946. It was basically a

Yak-3 with the piston engine removed and an RD-10 installed in the forward fuselage. Air for the engine passed through a nose intake and the engine exhausted below the cut-away rear fuselage virtually below the pilot's cockpit. To ensure that no damage was caused to the rear fuselage from the running engine, the underside was covered by heat-resistant metal. Two 23mm NS-23 cannon provided nose armament. During trials it is said that Olga Yamschikova, a company employee, flew the aircraft, which would have made her the first woman in the world to fly a jet fighter.

In 1947 the Yak-15 entered service with the IA-PVO, to become the first jet fighter operated by the Soviet air forces. It is believed to have had a maximum speed of 786 km/h (488 mph), although some reports suggested a figure slightly over 805 km/h (500 mph). From the start the Yak-3-type tailwheel landing gear had given trouble, even though the tailwheel itself was all-metal and for this reason it was subsequently decided to adapt the Yak-15 to have a nosewheel gear. A similar landing gear was used on the follow-on Yak-17, basically an improved Yak-15 powered by the developed 1000kg (2204lb) thrust RD-10A turbojet. A tandem two-seat version, known as the Yak-17UTI, became the first Soviet jet trainer. The Yak-17 remained operational long enough to receive the NATO reporting name *Feather* and possessed a maximum speed of 830 km/h (515.5 mph). Including two-seaters, 430 Yak-17s were built, a few going to Czechoslovakia and Poland. It is of interest to note that the Yak-16 was not a fighter but a ten-passenger transport aircraft with piston engines.

In order to obtain the best possible results from the basic Yak-15/17 shape and yet to compete with more radical fighter prototypes being designed to use the Soviet-built versions of the British Nene and Derwent engines, Yakovlev produced its Yak-23. This can be viewed as the definative development of the first generation fighter. As well as being of all-metal con-struction, the Yak-23 airframe was virtually completely revised, the most obvious external change being the mid-mounted tailplane. As with the Yak-17, wingtip fuel tanks helped to increase range. Power was provided by the RD-500, the 1600kg (3525lb) thrust Soviet development of the Derwent turbojet. Although considerably heavier than the previous Yak jets, the extra power of the RD-500 allowed a maximum speed of more than 965 km/h (600 mph). Remarkably armament remained light. More than 300 Yak-23s were produced, entering service with the air force in 1948 and later being acquired in small numbers by Czechoslovakia, Poland and other eastern bloc nations. However development of the MiG-15 curtailed the Yak-23's operational life in the Soviet Union, although it received the NATO reporting name *Flora*.

Among the last straight-winged jet

Below: the Avro CF-100 first flew in 1950 and the last examples remained in Canadian service until the 1980s.

fighters built was the Canadian Avro CF-100, which like so many other jet fighters began life on the power of a British engine. Design of the CF-100 began as early as 1946, but it was not until January 1950 that the first prototype took off for a flight, powered by two Rolls-Royce Avon turbojet engines mounted one each side of the fuselage at the wing roots. The two prototypes were known as Mk 1s, and were the only CF-100s so powered. Orenda Engines Ltd had formed out of the old A. V. Roe Canada gas turbine division, and in February 1949 first ran the prototype Orenda 1 axial-flow turbojet engine, two and a half years after design work had begun. An Orenda (a modified Orenda 1 known as the Orenda 3) was first flight tested on a North American F-86A Sabre in October 1950. The Orenda engine was then put into production as the Orenda 2. This engine had been developed specifically for the CF-100 and on 20 June 1951 the first preproduction Mk 2 fighter flew with Orenda 2s. The 2882kg (6355lb) thrust Orenda 9 was chosen as the power plant for the production CF-100 Mk 3, as it was suitable for installation in either left or right hand engine nacelles. First flown in October 1952, the CF-100 Mk 3, armed with eight 0.50in Colt-Browning machine-guns carried in a replaceable ventral tray, entered RCAF service in 1953. Altogether seventy Mk 3s were built, 50 later being converted into dual-control trainers.

When Mk 3s first entered service, they were the RCAF's first all-weather fighters and the first and only production jet fighters of indigenous design and manufacture. In total 692 CF-100s were built in various models, including prototypes. Among these were 3300kg (7275lb) thrust Orenda 11-powered CF-100 Mk 4Bs, armed with 48 2.75in air-to-air rockets, and similarly-powered CF-100 Mk 5s of 1955, with 52 rockets in each wingtip pod (Scorpion fashion). Fifty-three ex-RCAF CF-100 Mk 5s also served with the Belgian Air Force. Maximum speed of the CF-100 Mk 4B and Mk 5 was 1046 km/h (650 mph), the fighter having already become the first straight-winged jet fighter to exceed the speed of sound (on 18 December 1952). Although retired as combat aircraft in 1963, Canadian CF-100s continued flying into the 1980s, when a few Mk 5s were still listed as being used by the Canadian Armed Forces for utility and electronic countermeasures training roles. However by 1981 these had been retired.

Similar longevity has befallen the Soviet-designed Mikoyan-Gurevich MiG-15 and

the US-designed North American F-86 Sabre, which can be regarded as the first of the second-generation jet fighters. The earlier described Saab-29 can also be termed 'second generation.' In the early 1980s MiG-15bis and MiG-15UTIs are still being operated as trainers, while the last few Sabres retain some measure of attack capability. Chapter Six covers the bulk of the jet fighters built and flown in the 1950s, so why mention them here? Incredible as it might seem, the prototypes of the MiG-15

and Sabre first flew on 30 December 1947 and 1 October 1947 respectively, production aircraft of each type entering service in 1948 and 1949.

The Sabre became the USAF's first swept-wing fighter, and one of aviation history's all-time greats. But, in a classic 'chicken or egg' situation, it is a common misconception to believe that its naval counterpart, the FJ-2 Fury, was merely a derivative. The truth is far from this. Way back in 1944 North America had produced

the design of a straight-winged naval jet fighter, which eventually became the FJ-1 Fury, first flying in 1946. A USAAF derivative subsequently received the designation XP-86, but was known first by the company number N.A.140. This too had straight wings. Three prototypes were ordered as the war in Europe ended, two as flying prototypes. However material confiscated in Germany revealed many advanced aviation projects, including the use of swept wings, and before the end of the year the XP-86 had

been redesigned with swept wings and swept tail surfaces.

The two flying XP-86s were each engined by one 1700kg (3750lb) thrust Allison J35-C-3 turbojet mounted inside the oval-section fuselage, with a nose intake feeding air direct to the engine. The main fuel tanks were also located in the fuselage. The first flew on 1 October 1947. Both were later reengined with General Electric J47s, as selected for the first production model of the fighter. It was on the power of this

Above: the USAF's North American F-86A Sabre was blooded in combat with the MiG-15 over Korea.

engine that one XP-86 exceeded the speed of sound on 25 April 1948. To get this achievement into perspective, the world's first aircraft to fly faster than the speed of sound had only achieved this on 14 October 1947 and this aircraft was the purely experimental and rocket-powered Bell X-1.

The initial Sabre production version was

Above: the F-86D was the first all-weather fighter version of the Sabre, with a nose-mounted APG-37 radar.

Below: the F-86K was an all-weather fighter supplied to NATO allies. A Norwegian F-86K is pictured.

the P-86A, soon after its appearance receiving the new USAF designation F-86A. The first of more than 550 F-86As flew in May 1948, the 1st Fighter Group receiving Sabres from February of the following year. F-86As were powered successively by J47-GE-1, -3, -7, -9 and -13 engines, rated at 2360kg (5200lb) thrust. Armament comprised six 0.50in machine-guns in the nose, while provision was made for sixteen 5in rockets or jettisonable drop tanks under the wings.

On 15 September 1948 an F-86A broke the existing world speed record, held by the Douglas Skystreak, by achieving slightly over 1079 km/h (670 mph). Sabres of the later 'D' version held the record until September 1953, when the British Hawker Hunter achieved 1170 km/h (727 mph).The 'A' went out of production in December

1950, but not before two had been made readily available to the Central Fighter Establishment of the RAF. Another F-86A was fitted and flown in America with a Canadian Orenda engine as part of that engine's development program.

There were no F-86Bs or F-86Cs as such, and the 'A' was followed on the production line at Los Angeles by the F-86E day fighter. Powered by J47-GE-13 engines, F-86Es differed from the previous model in having a 'flying tail,' in which the elevators and tailplane were designed to move differentially in coordination to allow in-flight trim, but in most other respects they were similar. United States production amounted to well over 300 aircraft.

Of the thousands of Sabres eventually built, the two main versions were the F-86D and F-86F. The former was the first all-

weather version, powered first by a J47-GE-17 engine and, on the last aircraft, by a 3470kg (7650lb) thrust J47-GE-33 engine, both types fitted with afterburners. The prototype F-86D flew for the first time on 22 December 1949 and the first production aircraft in March 1951. Apart from the change of engine, the F-86D introduced an under-nose air intake, allowing for a new rounded nose containing the APG-37 radar scanner for all-weather operation. Naturally the F-86D was longer than previous versions because of the new nose and armament also changed from guns to 24 Mighty Mouse air-to-air rockets carried in a retractable ventral tray. The last of just over 2500 'Ds' were delivered in September 1955, numbers going to other nations under MDAP (Mutual Defense Assistance Program).

The F-86F was even more numerous (just) and was a day fighter powered by the 2708kg (5970lb) thrust J47-GE-27. The first production 'F' flew in March 1952. Similar to the 'E' in many ways, this model introduced the so-called '6-3' wing, in which the leading-edges were of increased chord and small fences were fitted. This refinement and others gave the Sabre increased maneuverability at high altitude, an area in which the Soviet-built MiG-15s seemed to

excel during the Korean War, although at the expense of landing speed. The fallacy that Sabres were greatly superior to MiG-15s was partly caused by the 'F's' improved high-altitude performance and the Sabre's general availability.

In truth the MiG had a tighter turning circle at high altitude and better rate of climb, although it suffered stability and handling problems. It was the better trained pilots of the USAF that made the difference in Korea, although this does not reduce the credit due to the Sabre, which was in all respects an excellent fighter. The first pilot of a jet fighter to achieve five 'jet kills' and so become a 'jet ace' was Captain James Jabara of the 4th Fighter-Interceptor Wing USAF, who flew the Sabre, finishing the war with fifteen MiG-15s downed. Of the F-86Fs built, a large number went to other air forces under MDAP and Mitsubishi of Japan produced F-86Fs and three-camera reconnaissance RF-86Fs under license.

The F-86H was basically a fighter-bomber development of the F-86F, powered by a 4218kg (9300lb) thrust General Electric J73-GE-3 engine. It had a 15cm (6in) deeper fuselage, larger tailplane without dihedral, greater length, electrically-operated flaps, hydraulically-operated speed brakes and controls, refined ejector seat for the pilot, strengthened landing gear, improved mechanism for carrying drop tanks together with rockets and bombs and fixed armament increased during production from six guns to four 20mm M-39 cannon. The first prototype flew on 30 April 1953 and 473 production examples were built between September 1953 and August 1955.

The final production version of the Sabre to be built in the United States was the F-86K, a J47-GE-33-powered update of the F-86D armed with four cannon for use by other NATO nations. North American produced 120, these going almost equally to the Netherlands and Norway, while a further 221 were assembled under license by Fiat in Italy for the Italian air force and others in Europe. The final piloted model of the Sabre was the F-86L, 981 of which were completed by modification from F-86Ds. Apart from its new slotted wing leading edge and new wingtips, which increased the span, it incorporated 'data link' equipment to receive information from the SAGE (Semi-Automatic Ground Environment) electronic air defense monitoring computer regarding intercept instructions. The only other model of the Sabre to follow the 'L' was the QF-86, the designation of surplus USAF aircraft operated as target drones.

In Australia the Commonwealth Aircraft Corporation produced 111 production Sabres powered by Rolls-Royce Avon engines and these were the fastest Sabres with maximum speeds of about 1125 km/h (700 mph), compared with the F-86A's 1086 km/h (675 mph) and F-86F's 1105 km/h (687

Left: the North American Sabre was license-built in Canada, a total of 1815 being produced by Canadair.

mph). So good were these that, when replaced by French Dassault Mirage IIIs, a number were acquired by the Indonesian air force, with whom they remained until 1978.

Canadair license-built the Sabre between 1950 and 1958, eventually producing 1815 for the RCAF and other air forces as Sabre Mk 2s (based on the F-86E and with the J47 engine), Sabre Mk 4s (similar to the Mk 2), Sabre Mk 5s (2950kg;6500lb thrust Orenda 10 engines and '6-3' wings) and Sabre Mk 6s (3270kg; 7210lb thrust Orenda 14 engines), plus Mk 1 and Mk 3 prototypes.

As mentioned earlier, the Soviet counterpart of the Sabre was the MiG-15, an excellent fighter with high performance made

Below: the Mikoyan-Gurevich MiG-15bis was built in Poland, where it was known as the LiM-2.

possible by the production of the RD-45 (Rolls-Royce Nene) engine at Moscow's No 45 factory. Whilst it is true that the MiG-15 owed its early success to the Nene engine, it should not be forgotten that the original specification under which it was designed was issued in early 1946, well before Britain delivered Nene and Derwent engines to the Soviet Union. It can be seen as a measure of the importance the Soviet Union placed on turbojet-powered aircraft, that it initiated this fighter competition so soon after the first competitions.

The Lavochkin prototype has already been mentioned. Yakovlev produced its Yak-30, which was a complete breakaway from the Yak-15 style of fighter and indeed looked very like the MiG. The MiG prototype was known as the I-310 and first flew on the second to last day of 1947 on the power of one of the original Nene engines from

Britain. A program of intensive evaluation and testing followed, matched only by the speed at which the RD-45 engine was entering production.

Mikoyan-Gurevich was virtually guaranteed the production 'go-ahead,' for the I-310 was not only a sound design but could be in production before Lavochkin and Yakovlev had prototypes ready. Production MiG-15s, initially powered by 2200kg (4850lb) thrust engines but after a short time by developed 2270kg (5004lb) thrust RD-45Fs, entered service in 1948. Armament comprised one 37mm N-37 and two 23mm NS-23 cannon in the nose, supplemented optionally by two bombs, rockets or drop tanks. The very first MiG-15s may have had two 12.7mm guns instead of the NS-23s.

Later receiving the NATO reporting name *Fagot*, the MiG-15 had mid-set wings, swept at an angle of 42 degrees at the lead-

ing edge. Two fences were attached to each wing. The circular-section fuselage was built in two main parts and the nose air intake was divided to channel air past the fuel tanks in the mid fuselage. Early fighters did not have a pilot ejection seat, but this later became a standard feature in the pressurized cockpit. Avionics comprised only a high-frequency radio and a homing receiver.

In addition to entering Soviet service, MiG-15s were supplied to North Korea and China, enabling the well documented and classic dogfights between the well-matched MiGs and Sabres from early in the Korean war. MiG-15s were also put into production in Czechoslovakia and Poland, as S-102 and LiM-1 fighters respectively.

During 1950 the original MiG-15 was replaced on production lines by the improved MiG-15bis. The main difference was in power plant, with the MiG-15bis using the 2700kg (5952lb) thrust Klimov VK-1, a further development of the Nene. Other changes included the use of perforated wing flaps, increased internal fuel capacity and more and improved avionics. Yet a reduced structural weight was achieved. Maximum speed was 1076 km/h (668 mph) and it was capable of carrying two 100kg, 250kg or 500kg bombs, rockets or 400 liter (88 Imperial gallon) drop tanks. Production lines in Czechoslovakia and Poland built S-103s and LiM-2s respectively.

In addition to the standard MiG-15 fighters, there appeared the MiG-15P all-weather version carrying Izumrud radar, the MiG-15Sbis high-altitude fighter, the MiG-15bisR armed photographic reconnaissance aircraft and the tandem two-seat MiG-15UTI trainer. The trainer, which was also built in Czechoslovakia as the CS-102,

Poland as the SBLiM-1 and in China, is the only version of the MiG-15 in widespread use today. It is worth mentioning that MiG-15bis and MiG-15UTIs completed in China were the first jets built there and that several hundred remain in use.

The MiG-15 can be viewed by historians as the springboard of modern Soviet fighter design, preparing the ground for the MiG-17, MiG-19, the most widely flown MiG-21, the swing-wing MiG-23 and the fastest fighter in the world, the MiG-25, known to NATO as *Foxbat*. But what of Lavochkin, Sukhoi and Yakovlev? After the La-15 the former name never again appeared on a production fighter. It took Sukhoi a decade to get a jet fighter into production and about as long for Yakovlev to follow its Yak-23 with a new fighter, in fact the Soviet Union's first two-seat all-weather fighter powered by two turbojet engines, as the Yak-25.

4: STRANGE SHAPES IN THE SKY

se of the jet engine was in its infancy when designers began to consider matching the new and highly-exciting power plant with equally non-conforming airframes. One company that saw the engine as not merely the power source for a conventional airframe was Northrop Aircraft, California, which during World War II had already begun developing aircraft with no fuselages or tail units as 'flying wings.' Most of the company's activities in this field centered around the development of huge-span flying-wing bombers, but it also developed an 11.58m (38ft) span experimental flying-wing

Overleaf: the Rockwell International XFV-12A is an experimental vertical/ short take-off fighter for the US Navy.

fighter, powered by two 522kg (1150lb) thrust Westinghouse J30 turbojet engines. The pilot occupied a cockpit in the center of the wing, lying in prone position so as not to spoil the overall shape of the wing. Designated XP-79B, this experimental fighter was intended to slice-off the tails of enemy bombers, using its high-strength welded magnesium wing. In the event, it went out of control on its first flight on 12 September 1945 and the project ended. However Northrop had much more success with its flying-wing bombers, which very nearly became the subject of large orders for the USAF.

Water-based jet fighters interested many designers postwar, the bombers and fighter-bombers in use at the end of World War II showing clearly the vulnerability of airfields to attack. Britain was among the

first to appreciate the possible uses for a sea-going jet fighter, although it should be said that conventionally-powered flying-boat fighters had been around since the early stages of World War I. Saunders-Roe designed the SR.A/1 to Air Ministry specification E.6/44. This was a bulky all-metal flying-boat with shoulder-mounted straight monoplane wings accommodating semi-retractable stabilizing floats. Power was provided initially by two 1474kg (3250lb) thrust Metropolitan-Vickers Beryl axial-flow turbojets mounted in side-of-fuselage fairings below the wings. The nose air intake was protected from spray during take-off and landing by a retractable fairing.

The SR.A/1 flew for the first time on 16 July 1947, so becoming the world's first jet-powered flying-boat. Three prototypes were built, the later two with slightly more powerful engines. Following a period of development and flight trials, the fighter was abandoned. The officially stated reason for not proceeding with production was the aircraft's lack of speed and maneuver-ability, caused by the deep and bulky hull. Whilst it must have been true that the SR.A/1 was less maneuverable than land-based jets, its speed of 824 km/h (512 mph) was fairly respectable. But, seen in context, even during World War I flying-boat fighters of Macchi-type managed to equal land-based fighters for speed and in the late 1940s and early 1950s there was every reason to believe that jet fighters were going to get faster very rapidly.

Another company that investigated the concept of a sea-going fighter was Convair, California, its delta-winged Sea Dart flying for the first time on 9 April 1953. Convair had pioneered delta wing research in the United States after World War II, helped by Dr Alexander Lippisch who had previously been researching along similar lines in Germany. On 18 September 1948 Convair flew its Model 7002, an experimental aircraft that had been built to investigate the flight characteristics of the projected F-92 fighter. When the F-92 program was cancelled, the experimental aircraft became the XF-92A, powered initially by one 2086kg (4600lb) thrust Allison J33-A-23 turbojet engine and later by an afterburning

Above left: the Saunders-Roe SR.A/1 was the world's first jet-powered flying boat and first flew in 1947.

Left: the Convair XF-92A experimental fighter evaluated the delta wing later used for the F-102 interceptor.

3720kg (8200lb) thrust J33-A-29. The delta wing form of the XF-92A was used subsequently by Convair for its Sea Dart and F-102 Delta Dagger fighters.

The Sea Dart itself was an experimental seaplane fighter, powered in original form by two 1542kg (3400lb) thrust Westinghouse J34-WE-42 turbojet engines. Accommodating a single pilot, it was expected to float in the water as a flying-boat during its first stages of take off, thereafter, and at a particular speed, a retractable hydroski or two hydroskis being lowered to lift the hull from the water prior to lift-off. After take off the hydroski or hydroskis were retracted back into the underside of the aircraft, allowing the Sea Dart to have a fairly normal fuselage and so maintain a high rate of maneuverability. A small number of refined Westinghouse J46-powered Sea Darts were built to extend the test program. Nevertheless the Sea Dart remained experimental,

although one had achieved Mach 1 in a shallow dive, the first seaplane to do so. So despite early promise, water-based jet fighters have never been part of an air force's inventory.

Convair was also one of two companies contracted by the US Navy to construct prototype vertical take-off and landing (VTOL) fighters, for possible use from naval vessels not fitted with conventional aircraft carrier decks. We now know that it took the British Sea Harrier (via the Hawker Siddeley Kestrel) and the Soviet Yakovlev Yak-36MP to master the naval VTOL combat aircraft role, but in the early 1950s the technology was not there to produce such advanced designs. Instead Convair, and its rival for orders Lockheed, produced what became termed 'tail-sitters.' The basic approach for the Convair XFY-1 Pogo and for the XFV-1 Vertical Riser was that the wings and tail surfaces, or the tail surfaces alone, would

Above: the Convair Sea Dart made use of hydroskis to achieve waterborne take-off from a flying boat hull.

form a cruciform shape, thereby allowing the aircraft to rest on castor wheels while pointing upward. The pilot of each aircraft sat on a gimballed (tilting) seat, so that he could assume a semi-upright position for take-off and landing, while sitting in a conventional position during normal horizontal flight. Power was provided by one Allison YT40-A-14 and one YT40-A-6 turboprop engine respectively on the Pogo and Vertical Riser, each engine driving co-axial contra-rotating propellers. It had been Dr Griffith, as mentioned in the first chapter, who had first suggested using a turbine not only to produce jet efflux but to drive a propeller via a reduction gear, back in 1926. Few fighters were actually designed to use turboprop engines, but an example of a highly-successful exponent of the turbo-prop was the British Westland Wyvern carrier-borne strike fighter of the 1950s. The Lockheed XFV-1 Vertical Riser was the more conventional of the two experimental fighters (the term 'conventional' being relative) by having straight wings as well as cruciform tail surfaces. However it was actually the least successful, first flying in March 1954 but achieving only horizontal flight before being cancelled.

The Convair XFY-1 Pogo first flew in August 1954 and in the course of the flight test program achieved its first transition from vertical to horizontal flight and back again on 2 November the same year. In typical Convair fashion, the Pogo had delta wings and smaller tail surfaces. However this aircraft too was subsequently abandoned, ending this particular US Navy program.

Several countries attempted to come up with successful VTOL designs for use on land, these including Germany's VFW-Fokker VAK 191B tactical reconnaissance fighter and the French Dassault Mirage III-V. The former first flew on 10 September 1971 and was powered by two Rolls-Royce RB.162-81 lift-jets mounted vertically in the fuselage and one horizontally-mounted RB.193-12 vectored-thrust engine for forward propulsion. Maximum speed was subsonic. It failed to enter production as a Fiat G91 replacement.

The Mirage III-V was the proposed VTOL variant of the production Mirage III fighter. Following on from the earlier Dassault Balzac research aircraft, which first flew in October 1962, the Mirage III-V was basically a lengthened and SNECMA TF-104, TF-106 or Pratt & Whitney TF30 turbofan-engined III-E, fitted with eight Rolls-Royce RB.162-1 lift-jet engines in the center section of the fuselage and covered by hinged doors. Two Mirage III-Vs were built, the first transition from horizontal to vertical flight being performed on 24 March 1966, but this variant of the highly-successful Mirage III remained experimental.

A modern US Navy program to evolve a new form of V/STOL (Vertical/Short Take-off and Landing) fighter and attack aircraft was initiated in the 1970s, resulting in the design and construction of the Rockwell

Right: the Lockheed XFV-1 Vertical Riser was one of two 'tail sitters' developed for the US Navy.

Far right: the Convair XFY-1 Pogo competed with the XFV-1 to meet the VTOL naval fighter requirement.

International XFV-12A. A single-seater with rear-mounted main wings and canard surfaces, the XFV-12A is powered by one modified 13,600kg (30,000lb) thrust Pratt & Whitney F401-PW-400 turbofan engine. For normal flight this horizontally-mounted engine exhausts from the rear tailpipe, but for vertical flight a valve closes this exit point, the efflux being diverted downward through ducts in the canards and wings.

Mixed with these gases is drawn-in ambient air, which results in greater thrust. Maximum speed of the XFV-12A is hoped to be approximately Mach 2. Unfortunately, funding shortages caused by defense program cutbacks has slowed progress.

Like France with its Mirage III-V, the Soviet Union attempted to increase the versatility of standard fighters using lift-jets. At the 1967 air display at Domodedovo,

three experimental STOL fighters and a VTOL type were flown. The Mikoyan MiG-21 (NATO *Fishbed-G*) and Mikoyan *Faithless* each used single main engines and two vertically-mounted lift-jets installed in tandem in the fuselage center section to achieve STOL performance, while the larger STOL aircraft based on the Sukhoi Su-15 (NATO *Flagon-B*) had two main engines and three lift-jets. All of these re-

mained experimental, as did the VTOL research aircraft flown during the display and
built by Yakovlev. The Yak operated on the
power of two forward-mounted turbojet
engines, exhausting through large vectored-thrust nozzles. During the display it
performed a full transition from vertical to
horizontal flight and vice versa and at one
point made a high-speed but subsonic dash
flight. Known to NATO as *Freehand* (the 'F'

reporting name indicating a fighter role –
albeit experimental), it helped Yakovlev
develop the far more sophisticated Yak-
36MP, which uses a mixture of the power
plant installations found on these STOL and
VTOL types.

Although most of the Soviet, French and
German aircraft described previously had
mixtures of horizontally and vertically-
mounted engines, all the engines them-

selves were conventional turbojets or
turbofans. Aircraft with truly 'mixed' power
plants have been built, at the time of their
appearance seeming to offer solutions to
the problem of attaining high performance.

As described in chapter five, the Ryan

**Below: the Dassault Mirage III-V made
use of fuselage-mounted lift-jets for
hovering flight**

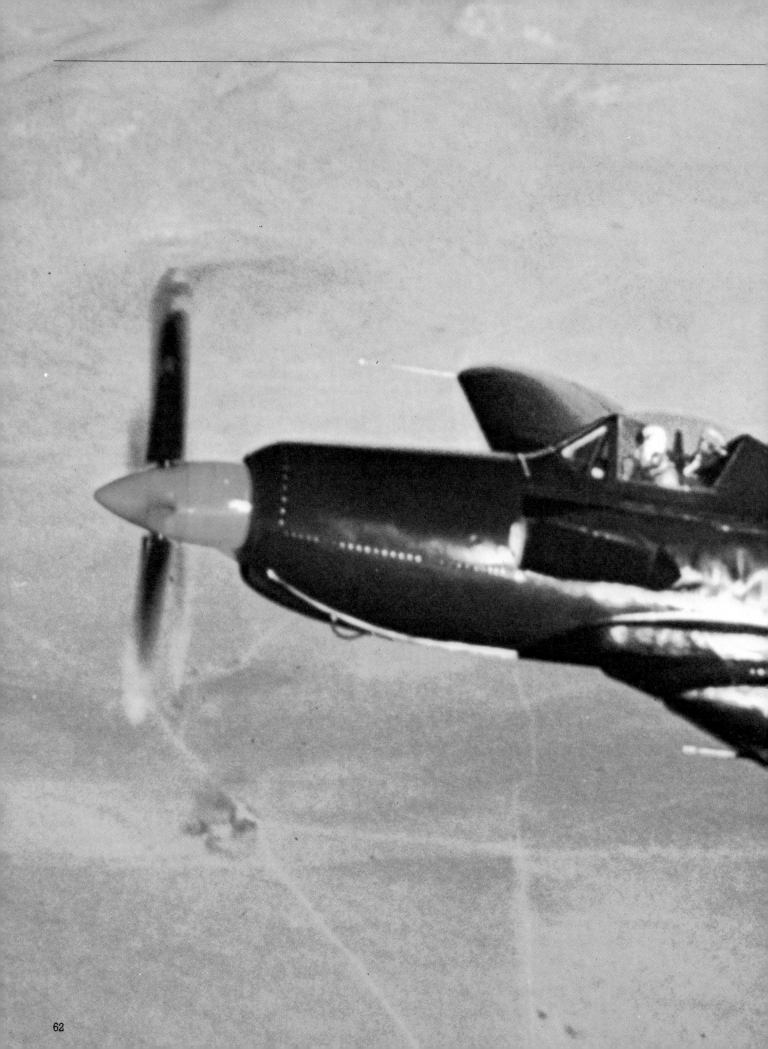

Below: the Ryan XF2R-1 Dark Shark was
powered by a nose-mounted turboprop
and a turbojet in the rear fuselage.

Fireball was built in very limited numbers as a mixed-power naval fighter. During production four Fireball airframes were assigned for experimental use, one becoming the XF2R-1 Dark Shark. First flown in November 1946, the Dark Shark had the usual General Electric J31 turbojet installed in the rear fuselage, but the nose-mounted engine was the new General Electric TG-100, a 2200shp, plus 272kg (600lb) thrust, turboprop engine which received the designation XT31-GE-2. The TG-100 was the first all-American tuboprop engine and was intended to power the aircraft during all phases of flight, except when increased speed was required for combat. Maximum speed of the one-off Dark Shark was approximately 805 km/h (500 mph).

In America Republic flew its experimental Mach 1 turbojet and rocket-powered XF-91 interceptor in 1949, featuring also variable-incidence and inverse-tapering swept wings, and Britain built and flew a turbojet and rocket-powered interceptor in the form of the experimental Mach 2.4 Saunders-Roe S-R.53, which first flew on 16 May 1957. However the French were the main protagonists of mixed power. One such aircraft was designed in the latter 1940s as the Sud-Ouest SO 9000 Trident, a mixed-power research aircraft that was intended to lead to the development of a similarly-powered interceptor. The original Trident was a fairly unspectacular aircraft, with straight constant-chord wings and a circular-section fuselage ending with an all-moving three surface tail unit. Power was initially provided by two 400kg (880lb) thrust Turboméca Marboré II turbojets installed in wingtip pods, subsequently replaced by Dassault M.D.30 Viper ASV.5s with twice the power. On the power of the Marboré IIs, the Trident first flew on 2 March 1953. Prior to the change to Vipers a 4500kg (9921lb) thrust SEPR.481 rocket motor had been installed in the tail, a flight being achieved in this form on 4 September the following year. During the spring of 1955

stroyed in an accident when the rocket fuel exploded. By the time of the accident the first of six preproduction Trident II interceptors had already flown on 3 May 1957, indicating a maximum speed of very nearly Mach 2. One Trident II, powered by 1100kg (2425lb) thrust Turboméca Gabizo turbojets and an SEPR 631 rocket motor, established a new world altitude record by reaching 24,217m (79,452ft) on 2 May 1958, bettering the previous record, set by a Grumman F11F-1 Tiger a fortnight before, by nearly 800 meters. Actual production Trident interceptors were not built, the program having been abandoned due to defense cutbacks.

Left: the Sud-Ouest Trident was an experimental mixed-power aircraft, with turbojet and rocket motors. It is now displayed at Le Bourget.

Below: the Saunders-Roe S-R.53 was a British mixed-power interceptor, which was not produced for the RAF.

it broke the sound barrier while in a shallow dive, followed soon after by Mach 1 flight while climbing.

The Trident had achieved Mach 1 on nothing like full power, so the decision was taken to develop the SO 9050 Trident II as the prototype of a lightweight interceptor. Two were ordered, one of which was de-

Above: the Griffon II combined turbojet and ramjet power and is shown on display at Le Bourget.

Right: the McDonnell XF-85 Goblin was a parasite fighter, which was to be carried by the B-36 bomber.

This was undoubtedly the right decision for another reason. In view of the far more advanced design of the British S-R.53, which would have carried Firestreak air-to-air missiles at the wingtips and had much higher speed, the Trident would have been out-of-date before entering service.

Another French experimental aircraft of the mid-1950s from which it might have been possible to develop an interceptor, hence the subsequent interest shown by the USAF, was the Nord 1500 Griffon II. This was little more than a huge combination power plant around which was fitted a pilot's cockpit, delta wings and a vertical tail. In fact the Griffon II was the modified turbojet only-powered Griffon I, fitted with a 3400kg (7495lb) thrust SNECMA Atar 101 turbojet engine installed inside a Nord-designed annular and integral ramjet.

The French Leduc experiments with ramjet-powered aircraft from the late 1940s, had proved the power obtainable from this form of power plant, but as a ramjet will not operate until high-velocity air is introduced through the duct, René Leduc's early aeroplanes had to be air-launched. He had expected to construct an interceptor version of his aircraft under French military contract, but this work ended after official support had been withdrawn. In fact the Griffon II first flew in the same year as Leduc's experiments were terminated in 1957. However Leduc had expected his interceptor to take off under its own power, using an Atar turbojet in combination, there-

after igniting the ramjet. It was this system that was used by the Griffon II. The Griffon's ramjet developed 4170kg (9193lb) thrust at an altitude of 15,240m (50,000ft), allowing for a very high maximum speed but which had to be kept at just over Mach 2 because of the limitation posed by the construction of the airframe. Therefore despite early promise, no production aircraft has ever had a ramjet as its primary power plant, although it has been used on missiles, an example being the British Bloodhound.

Another aircraft that, like the Griffon II, had an engine seemingly disproportionate in size to its overall dimensions, was the McDonnell XF-85 Goblin. Development of this fighter began in 1945, as one of the proposed defense systems for the Consolidated-Vultee B-36 six-engined intercontinental strategic bomber. Known as a parasite fighter, it was intended to be carried in the forward bomb-bay of the B-36. When threatened by interceptor attack, it was envisioned that the bomber would lower the Goblin out of the bay by means of a 'trapeze,' the fighter subsequently being recovered again by the use of a special retractable 'sky hook' carried in front of the pilot's cockpit. The hook-on technique had already served the United States well, when in the 1930s Curtiss Sparrowhawk biplane fighters had operated from US Navy airships.

The Goblin itself was built around a 1360kg (3000lb) thrust Westinghouse J34-WE-22 turbojet engine and had swept

Left: a model of Grumman's FSW (forward swept wing) demonstrator aircraft.

wings of only 6.47m (21ft 2¾in) span that could be folded. Six individual surfaces made up the tail unit and armament comprised five forward-firing guns. With a total length of only 4.53m (14ft 10½in) and a height of 2.52m (8ft 3¼in), it could easily fit into the B-36's bomb bay.

The concept of using a jet fighter to hook onto a fast bomber was proved by tests with a modified P-80 Shooting Star and a B-29 bomber and the Goblin was taken up by the specially adapted B-29 for its first free flight on 23 August 1948. Flying over the Muroc test base, the fighter was released. At an altitude of 7620m (25,000ft) the Goblin attempted to hook back on to the trapeze, but rough conditions caused the fighter to rise suddenly as it neared the trapeze. The force of impact as the fighter struck the trapeze caused the cockpit canopy to smash, while the pilot lost both his helmet and oxygen mask. Although the pilot had the use of an ejection seat, he elected to attempt to land the Goblin on the desert sands below, having already put what remained of the oxygen hose into his mouth. At high speed, he put the Goblin down on its emergency-only landing skids. Remarkably only a bent ventral fin and one damaged wingtip resulted. After the addition of small fins on the wings to improve stability, several successful hook-ons were made. However for whatever reason, the parasite fighter concept for the production B-36 was dropped, although the success attained during later trials must have influenced a later decision to use a version of the Republic Thunderflash as a parasite reconnaissance aircraft, to provide reconnaissance models of the B-36 with a 'dash' plane to make the final reconnaissance over the target area. In a way, by allowing the B-36 to 'stand off' from the target area, the Thunderflash acted as protection for the motherplane.

Even today when money is short for experimentation into new technologies, new shapes are emerging. Will the fighter of the 1990s have forward-swept wings, as is being researched by Grumman. In 1983 there will appear the first modern jet-powered experimental aircraft with rear-mounted swept-forward wings and canards, said to offer improved maneuverability, be virtually impossible to spin, have less drag, and have many other benefits. Only time will tell!

5: AIR POWER AT SEA

In 1917 a light battle cruiser under construction for the Royal Navy was redesignated an aircraft carrier and modified accordingly. Appearing as HMS *Furious,* it was the world's first naval vessel designed to operate landplanes from its deck, being assigned six Sopwith Pup fighters and four seaplanes. Later accommodating thirty-three aircraft, HMS *Furious* was active again during the interwar period and World War II, finally being sent to the scrap yard in 1949.

By the outbreak of World War II some 20 aircraft carriers were operational with the navies of Britain, France, Japan and the United States. Those of Japan and the United States met in the epic battles of the Coral Sea and Midway in 1942, when an American airman sent out the famous message 'scratch one flat-top' following the destruction of a Japanese carrier. Construction of at least 11 other aircraft carriers had been underway in 1939. During this war carrier operations were widespread and included

the use of lower-cost and mass produced smaller escort carriers.

For the US Navy by far the most important carrier fighter of World War II was the Grumman F6F Hellcat. It first went into action in an attack on Marcus Island in September 1943, eventually accounting for nearly three-quarters of enemy aircraft destroyed by the Navy. Potentially even more potent was the Chance Vought F4U Corsair, which was flown by the US Marine Corps initially from land bases, as the

Overleaf: the USS *Enterprise* was the world's first nuclear-powered aircraft carrier.

fighter's landing speed was considered too high for use from carriers. The Royal Navy did not share this view and from 1944 operated the Corsair from its carriers, leading the way for America to follow.

Today the US Navy has by far the biggest and most powerful aircraft carrier force in the world, each vessel carrying what can be described as a small air force. This can be made up of two interceptor-fighter squadrons flying McDonnell Douglas F-4 Phantoms or Grumman F-14 Tomcats, two squadrons of Vought A-7 Corsair attack aircraft, one squadron of Grumman A-6 Intruder strike and tanker aircraft, plus Grumman EA-6B Prowler ECM and Grumman E-2 Hawkeye airborne early-warning and fighter control aircraft, one squadron of Lockheed S-3A Viking anti-submarine aircraft and Sikorsky SH-3 Sea King helicopters, approximately 90 aircraft in total.

The operation of jet fighters from aircraft carriers had a rather strange beginning, with Britain and the United States taking the early initiatives. Back in 1943 the design was started of a new fighter for the US Navy, intended to make use of both piston and jet engines. Eventually known as the Ryan FR-1 Fireball, it was to be flown as an ordinary Wright R-1820 piston-engined fighter for all flying except combat dash, when the General Electric J31 installed in the rear

Below: the Ryan FR-1 Fireball was powered by a piston engine, plus a rear-mounted turbojet.

fuselage would be used. At the beginning of 1945 a squadron had been commissioned to fly the first Fireballs and trials from USS *Ranger* started. However, this squadron saw no combat during World War II. With the end of the war most of the 700 aircraft ordered in total were cancelled. Of the 66 Fireballs completed, some were used for experimental work. Although remaining in use only until 1947, finally on board USS *Badoeng Strait,* one Fireball made aviation history, when on 6 November 1945 its piston engine failed as it was making an approach to USS *Wake Island* and the pilot landed on jet power alone. This was the first occasion an aircraft using jet power had landed on a carrier, preempting the first pure jet fighter landings and take offs by a British de Havilland Vampire, to and from HMS *Ocean* by nearly a month. The Fireball had a maximum speed of 684km/h (425mph).

Whilst the British Sea Vampire became the Fleet Air Arm's first jet fighter (but not standardized in first-line service), its US equivalent was not a variant of a land-based fighter, but had been designed from the outset for naval operations. A contract to produce a prototype carrier fighter designated XFD-1 had been given to the McDonnell Aircraft Corporation in January 1943, the first of two XFD-1's flying two years later. In the following March the fighter was ordered into production as the FH-1 Phantom, becoming McDonnell's first indigenous aircraft to be series built.

On 21 July 1946 a prototype Phantom landed on board USS *Franklin D. Roosevelt,* so becoming the first US pure jet fighter to land on a carrier, and the sixty production FH-1s were operated thereafter for a brief period. Powered by two 727kg (1600lb) thrust Westinghouse J30-WE-20 turbojet engines installed in the wing roots, the Phantom had a maximum speed of 810km/h (505mph) and was armed with four 0.50in machine-guns in the nose plus optionally rockets carried under the low-mounted straight wings.

McDonnell followed the Phantom with its larger and more powerful F2H Banshee, prototypes of which had been ordered in the same month as the company had received the Phantom production order. Another straight-winged single-seater, the first Banshee prototype flew on 11 January 1947. The usual 56 production fighters were ordered as F2H-1 Banshees, each powered by two 1360kg (3000lb) thrust Westinghouse J34-WE-22 turbojets and these were delivered from early 1949. But this was just the beginning. By the close of production in

October 1953, no less than 892 Banshee fighters had been accepted by the US Navy and Marine Corps. The F2H-2 major production version with J34-WE-34 engines included night fighter and photographic-reconnaissance sub-variants.

Production was completed by the F2H-3 long-range and all-weather fighter and the

similar F2H-4, the latter receiving the most powerful engines fitted to the Banshee, in this case two 1633kg (3600lb) thrust J34-WE-38s. Armament comprised four nose-mounted 20mm cannon plus underwing weapons. The F2H-4 had a maximum speed of 981km/h (610mph), very much faster than earlier versions.

During the mid-1950s the Royal Canadian Navy took over the use of 39 F2H-3 Banshees, but by then the days of the straight-winged first-line fighter had nearly ended, even for navies. Of course straight-winged fighters other than those produced by McDonnell had entered US Navy service. Included in these were the Chance Vought F6U-1 Pirate (30 delivered from August 1949, with one Westinghouse J34-WE-30A turbojet each), the North American FJ-1 Fury, Douglas F3D Skyknight and Grumman F9F Panther. But for its Banshee replacement McDonnell designed the swept-wing F3H Demon.

The Demon was a complete break away from traditional design for McDonnell, undoubtedly helped by the design and construction of the experimental XF-88 land penetration fighter during the latter 1940s. Like the XF-88, which, in XF-88A form with afterburning, formed the basis for the USAF's F-101 Voodoo fighter, the Demon had very thin and swept wings and tail surfaces. However, unlike the XF-88, the Demon had an all-moving tailplane mounted below the fin and rudder, air intakes each side of the forward fuselage (instead of in the wing roots) and was powered by a single engine exhausting below the tail.

The first prototype XF3H-1 Demon flew on 7 August 1951. A year later an order for 150 production examples was placed, each aircraft to be powered by one 3266kg (7200lb) thrust Westinghouse J40-WE-22 turbojet. However, during development of the fighter to increase its operational capability, its weight rose from 9980kg (22,000lb) to 13,154kg (29,000lb), which left the fighter somewhat underpowered. Therefore only the first 56 production Demons used this engine. The remainder switched to the 4310kg (9500lb) thrust Allison J71-A-2, after failure of the J40-WE-24 expected replacement, as such becoming F3H-2s. Of the 56 F3H-1s, 21 were used as trainers and 29 were subsequently reengined with J71s.

The main production version of the Demon was the F3H-2, armed with four 20mm cannon and optional external stores. Sub-variants included the F3H-2N night and all-weather fighter, carrying also four AIM-9C Sidewinder air-to-air missiles and with provision for drop-tanks and nuclear weapons, and the F3H-2M day missile fighter carrying four AIM-7C Sparrow III air-to-air missiles. A projected version of the Demon was the F3H-2P photographic-reconnaissance aircraft. Altogether more than 500 Demons were built, serving in diminishing numbers until the mid-1960s, when the remaining fighters carried F-3 designations.

The Demon gave way to the mighty F-4 Phantom II, the US Navy's first Mach 2

Above far left: the McDonnell F2H Banshee first flew in January 1947 and entered service two years later.

Above left: the first American pure jet fighter to land on a carrier was the McDonnell FD-1 Phantom. This is an artist's impression.

Left: a McDonnell F3H Demon about to leave the flight deck of its parent carrier.

fighter and undoubtedly one of aviation's all-time greats. When first conceived in 1954, the Phantom II was to be a twin-engined all-weather attack aircraft, carrying the appropriate Navy designation AH-1. In the following year its role was changed to that of missile fighter, whereupon prototypes were ordered as tandem two-seat XF4H-1s. The first XF4H-1 flew on 26 May 1955. After early trials had necessitated some changes to the airframe, the aircraft took on its now familiar look, with low-mounted wings that were virtually a cross between swept and delta and incorporating outer panels with considerable dihedral. Its tailplane had massive anhedral, ahead and below which the two J79 turbojet engines exhausted. Both intake and nozzle areas of the ducts accommodating the engines were fully variable. Altogether 23 pre-production and 24 early production aircraft were produced for the Navy as F4H-1Fs with J79-GE-2 engines, subsequently being redesignated

F-4A Phantom IIs and carrying normally four Sparrow III missiles recessed into the fuselage underside. The first major production version was the F-4B (originally F4H-1), powered by two J79-GE-8 turbojets. This became a standard all-weather fighter with the US Navy and Marine Corps, 649 eventually being built. Normal armament comprised six Sparrow III or eight Sidewinder missiles, although up to 7257kg (16,000lb) of other weapons could be carried beneath the wings and fuselage. Of the production total, twelve temporarily became F-4Gs with data link communications equipment for use in Vietnam from USS *Kitty Hawk,* while more recently 227 have been updated as F-4Ns, redelivery taking place from 1973. Similar to the F-4B but without dual controls or missiles is the RF-4B, the USMC multisensor reconnaissance variant of which 46 were built as such.

In 1966 McDonnell flew an improved version of the F-4B, the F-4J, which like the

earlier Phantom II was intended primarily as a US Navy/USMC interceptor but with much improved ground attack capability. Power was provided by two 8119kg (17,900lb) thrust J79-CE-10 turbojets. Its landing speed was lowered by the use of drooping ailerons and a slotted tail, despite the fact that its weight had increased substantially. Five hundred and eighteen were built, although many have been modified to F-4S standard to extend the aircraft's useful life, changes including a strengthened structure, the use of newly-designed leading-edge slats and other updates to the airframe and avionics. Redelivery began in 1978. The only other navy to fly Phantom IIs was the Royal Navy, which received 52 F-4Ks. Designated Phantom FG.Mk 1 in British service, the first squadron was declared operational in 1969. However, with the decommissioning of HMS *Ark Royal,* the Royal Navy Phantom IIs were passed to the RAF. Similar to the US F-4B, the F-4K incor-

Below: the Phantom FG.Mk. 1 was a
Rolls-Royce Spey engined version of the
F-4 for the Fleet Air Arm.

Above: the Northrop YF-17 lightweight
fighter was developed in competition
with the General Dynamics F-16.

porates some improvements developed for the F-4J, and other refinements, and is powered by two 9305kg (20,515lb) thrust with afterburning Rolls-Royce Spey RB.168-25R Mk 201 turbofan engines.

By the end of Phantom II production in the United States in October 1979, 5057 had been built. Of these the US Navy and USMC had received a staggering 1264. However, twice this number had been acquired by the USAF and the remainder had been exported. Air Force versions are described in chapter six.

The very latest McDonnell Douglas combat aircraft for naval use are the AV-8B (described with the BAe Sea Harrier) and the F/A-18 Hornet. Developed out of the Northrop YF-17 lightweight fighter, which was formerly under development as a rival for the General Dynamics YF-16 for USAF orders, the single-seat Hornet was conceived by Northrop and McDonnell Douglas jointly, the latter company becoming prime contractor. However, it is not a lightweight fighter, but a full carrier-based naval strike fighter to replace the F-4 Phan-

Below: the Douglas F3D-2Q Skyknight, displayed in California, was modified for electronic countermeasures.

Above: the McDonnell Douglas F/A-18 Hornet will become the standard US Navy carrier-based strike fighter.

tom II, McDonnell Douglas A-4 Skyhawk light attack bomber and the Vought A-7 Corsair II attack aircraft.

It had been intended originally to produce two separate versions of the Hornet for fighter and attack roles, as the F-18 and A-18 respectively, but the types became so alike that a single Hornet was then proposed under the production designation F/A-18A. The TF/A-18A is the tandem two-seat training version, while the Canadian Armed Forces ordered the Hornet to replace its CF-101s and CF-104s under the designation CF-18.

The F/A-18A Hornet itself is powered by two 7257kg (16,000lb) thrust General Electric F404-CE-400 low bypass turbofan engines and is characterized by its twin outward-canted fins and rudders. Maximum speed is more than Mach 1.8. Armament as a fighter includes two Sidewinder missiles carried at the wingtips and up to four Sparrows attached underwing and on the air intakes. In an attack role up to 7710kg (17,000lb) of weapons can be carried. A nose-mounted 20mm M61 six-barrel

cannon is standard.

The first of 11 development Hornets took to the air initially on 18 November 1978 and sea trials followed in 1979. Low volume production began soon after, with the US Navy receiving its first few production Hornets for evaluation during 1980-81. Initial operational capability for the Hornet with the US Navy was planned for 1982, when deliveries to Canada were to begin.

It was during the production of the F-4 Phantom II that the name of the manufacturer changed from the McDonnell Aircraft Company to the McDonnell Douglas Corporation, when McDonnell merged with the Douglas Aircraft Company (in 1967). Douglas itself had been involved in the production of jet fighters for the US Navy and Marine Corps since the late 1940s, its first success being the F3D Skyknight. As mentioned earlier, the Skyknight was just one of several straight-winged fighters operated by the US Navy/USMC, but was unique in having side-by-side seats for the pilot and radar operator. First flown on 23 March 1948, it was armed with four 20mm cannon, although provision was made for attack weapons to be carried underwing. A dozen were also subsequently updated to carry air-to-air missiles as F3D-1Ms. During

its career the Skyknight recorded several 'firsts', including the first MiG-15 shot down at night during the Korean War, and during the early 1960s became the first tactical ECM jet aircraft. As an ECM type it remained in service long enough to be deployed in Vietnam, by which time all remaining Skyknights had received F-10 designations.

Most of the 265 Skyknights built were of the slightly more-powerful F3D-2 variant, using two 1542kg (3400lb) thrust Westinghouse J34-WE-36 turbojets mounted Scorpion-style on the lower fuselage sides, beneath the wings. But for its follow-on fighter design Douglas abandoned straight wings and conventional tail surfaces for a form of slightly swept and rounded delta wings and a vertical tail only. These very low aspect ratio wings were seen as best to combine a high rate of climb and good maneuverability with reasonable landing speeds. This layout was retained for the later Skylancer fighter, of which four development aircraft only were built as F5D-1s from 1956. But, as originally evolved, this configuration was used on the F4D Skyray, the first prototype of which first flew on 23 January 1951 on the power of a rear fuselage-mounted Allison J35-A-17 turbojet.

Left: the Grumman F9F Panther was the first US Navy jet to go into combat, during the Korean War.

Below: this Grumman F9F Panther carries 5in rockets under its wings for ground attack.

Right: a Douglas F4D-1 Skyray all-weather fighter is armed with Sidewinder air-to-air missiles.

The Skyray had been intended to be powered by a Westinghouse J40 turbojet and indeed the two prototypes flew with versions of the J40 during trials. The second, powered by a J40-WE-8 with afterburner, broke the world speed record on 3 October 1953 with a flight of 1212km/h (753mph) over a 3km course. But, despite this success, the J40 engine did not meet its early promise and the 419 F4D-1 Skyrays for the US Navy/Marine Corps had either 6123kg (13,500lb) thrust (with afterburning) Pratt & Whitney J57-P-2 or 6577kg (14,500lb) thrust J57-P-8 engines. The first F4D-1 flew on 5 June 1954 but delivery to the Navy took nearly two more years. As with the other fighters flying in 1962, Skyrays were redesignated to conform to a new designation system, becoming F-6As. In addition to carrier use, the Skyray was flown with the North American Air Defense Command as an all-weather interceptor, in the hands of a US Navy squadron assigned to this role. It ended its operational career in about 1964, having been transferred to reserve units. Maximum speed was just over Mach 1 and armament comprised four 20mm cannon normally, but this could be complemented with up to 1814kg (4000lb) of attack weapons.

Douglas had had a close connection with the US Navy since the early 1920s, although mainly in the field of bombers and torpedo-bombers. Even closer Navy traditions has been the prize of the current Grumman Corporation, fighters built by the company under the earlier name Grumman Aircraft Engineering Corporation having been the mainstay of the Navy since the 1930s. These had included the FF-1 and later biplanes, the F4F Wildcat and the F6F Hellcat, of which the latter was rivalled by none during Navy actions of World War II.

In the long-held tradition by Grumman of using names of animals in the cat family for its fighters, its first jet fighter was known as the F9F Panther (following on from the Navy piston-engined F8F Bearcat). Originally conceived to be powered by no less than four Westinghouse 19XB-2B engines (J30s) in the wings, the design was changed to use one turbojet in the tail following the acquisition from Britain of two Rolls-Royce Nenes. In 1947 Pratt & Whitney Aircraft received a license to manufacture and sell the Nene in the United States, the first engines going to Grumman for the Panther. Pratt & Whitney

Right: the Grumman Cougar was the swept-wing version of the Panther: an F9F-8 with a radome beneath the nose is illustrated.

Nenes were known as JT-6B Turbo-Wasps, carrying the military designation J42s.

Of three Panther prototypes built, two flew with Nenes and one with an Allison J33. The first Nene-powered aircraft took to the air on 24 November 1947. Production was split between J42-P-6-powered F9F-2s and J33-A-8-powered F9F-3s, resulting in well over 400 aircraft. The first J42 and J33-powered production Panthers had flown in November and August 1948 respectively, by which time a 150 hour qualification test on the J42 at the Naval Air Material Center had proved a static thrust of 2268kg (5000lb). This was higher than the J33's 2087kg (4600lb) thrust. Indeed it was the highest publically-known thrust rating of any US engine at that time. In consequence, the F9F-2 proved to be the better fighter and F9F-3s, built to guard against J42 failure (the Navy having shown extra caution after its J30 episode), were later reengined with J42s.

No F9F-4s, which would have received Allison engines, were built. Instead the order for 73 was added to that for 580 Pratt & Whitney J48-engined F9F-5s. The J48 (Pratt & Whitney JT-7 Turbo-Wasp) was of very similar size to the J42, although rated at 2835kg (6250lb) thrust. It was similar to the British Rolls-Royce Tay, having been developed by both British and US companies. The main Pratt & Whitney contribution was probably the engine's afterburner, but the engine's main achievement was the ability

to take in 30 percent more air, made possible by a redesigned impeller and larger turbine blades. The F9F-5 was therefore the fastest version, with a maximum speed of 932km/h (579mph). Armament of all versions was four 20mm cannon, plus the provision for 5in rockets, bombs and other attack weapons. A photographic reconnaissance version became the F9F-5P.

The Panther has several claims to fame. It was Grumman's first jet fighter, the first jet fighter flown by the US Navy to see combat in Korea, the first Navy jet to destroy a MiG-15 during that war (on 9 November 1950) and the first Navy straight-winged jet fighter to be developed into a swept-wing type. Its swept-wing derivative was the F9F Cougar, of which 1985 examples were built if the 399 F9F-8T (later TF-9J) two-seat fighter-trainers are included. The first version to fly, on 20 September 1951, was the 3289kg (7250lb) thrust J48-P-8-engined F9F-6, followed by its unarmed photographic-reconnaissance equivalent, the F9F-6P. Next came the lower-powered 2880kg (6350lb) thrust Allison J33-A-16A-engined F9F-7, built in much smaller number. The last single-seaters were the faster and longer-range F9F-8 and F9F-8P, based on the F9F-6 and F9F-6P but with many refinements including increased fuel capacity in the slightly longer fuselage and the use of fixed cambered leading-edge extensions in place of the previous slats. The first F9F-8 flew on 18 January 1954, followed by the

F9F-8P on 21 August 1955. Interestingly the two-seat TF-9J Cougar was still in service as a combat and operational trainer in the early 1980s, capable of carrying rockets, bombs, four Sidewinder missiles or other stores, in addition to its two 20mm cannon.

Yet another development of the Panther was the F11F Tiger, although when this flew in prototype form on 30 July 1954 there was little to indicate this relationship. The Tiger was not very successful, with only about 200 being built for the Navy. A single 4763kg (10,500lb) thrust (with afterburning) Wright J65-W-18 turbojet engine powered all Tigers except for the prototypes, while all but the first 39 had extended noses to accommodate radar. In the event no radar was ever fitted, making the Tiger strictly a day fighter. Those which remained in 1962 were redesignated F-11As, but these were not in first line use, having been withdrawn in 1959. Nevertheless the Tiger managed a maximum speed of 1207km/h (750mph), could carry four Sidewinder missiles in addition to its four 20mm cannon, or could be used in a ground attack role. Interestingly an early Tiger fitted with a General

Above: the Grumman F11F-1 Tiger was a further development of the basic Panther design.

Right: a Grumman F-14A Tomcat fleet defense fighter prepares to catapult from a US carrier.

Electric J79 engine, as one of two experimental F11F-1Fs, set up a world altitude record in 1958 by reaching 23,449m (76,932ft), while it was reported in 1958 that Mitsubishi of Japan then expected to license-build the F11F for the JASDF.

The latest Grumman naval fighter is of course the F-14 Tomcat, which first flew in prototype form on 21 December 1970 and has become the US Navy's first multi-role fighter with variable-geometry wings. A two-seater, with the pilot and flight officer in tandem, the production F-14A has a maximum speed of about Mach 2.4 on the power of two 9480kg (20,900lb) thrust (with afterburning) Pratt & Whitney TF30-P-412A turbofan engines. Armament comprises one M61-A-1 Vulcan 20mm multibarrel gun, plus six Phoenix and two Sidewinder, or four Sidewinder and four Sparrow, or six Sparrow and two Sidewinder air-to-air missiles, or other weapons up to a maximum of 6577kg (14,500lb). The F-14A first joined the US Navy in 1972 and by September 1974 two squadrons were serving on board USS *Enterprise*. By the beginning of 1982 the Navy had received 416 F-14A Tomcats, while a further eighty had been exported to Iran by 1978 for air force use.

As mentioned earlier, Grumman was first

to use basically the same aircraft with straight and swept wings, but another company that achieved this successfully was North American Aviation. This company's first jet fighter was the FJ-1 Fury for the Navy, a contemporary of the F6U Pirate, and which beat the Panther into the air by a year. The first XFJ-1 Fury prototype flew for the first time on 27 November 1946, eventually being followed by thirty production FJ-1s to

serve on USS *Boxer*. Each production Fury was powered by a 1814kg (4000lb) thrust Allison J35 engine installed in the fuselage and fed with air from the large nose intake. Maximum speed was 880km/h (547mph), sufficient to interest the USAF also, leading to the development of the Air Force's swept-wing P-86 Sabre.

In a strange turn of events, from the Air Force's Sabre was developed the Navy's

Above: the North American F-1 Fury naval fighter was a parallel development to the USAF's F-86.

swept-wing Fury, the first FJ-2 Fury prototype being flown on 14 February 1952. Production FJ-2s for the USMC were similar to the USAF's F-86E and were each powered by one 2722kg (6000lb) thrust General Electric J47-GE-2 turbojet. The remainder of the 1115 swept-wing Furies built by 1958 was made up of FJ-3s and FJ-4s, powered by Wright J65 engines. The 3493kg (7700lb) thrust Wright J65-W-16A-powered FJ-4B possessed a maximum speed of 1094km/h (680mph); it was armed with four 20mm cannon plus four Side-winder missiles or bombs and other attack weapons optionally. The swept-wing Fury went to sea from 1954-55 with USMC and Navy squadrons, those remaining in 1962 receiving the new designation F-1.

Chance Vought's somewhat limited success with its F6U Pirate led the company to try and break new ground with its follow-up fighter. The result was the very unconventional F7U Cutlass, a swept-wing and tailless single-seater with combined ailerons and elevators (known as 'ailavators') and two fin

Below: a pair of LTV F-8 Crusaders prepare to catapult with wings in the high incidence position.

Above: the Chance Vought F7U Cutlass was the first US Navy production fighter able to exceed the speed of sound.

and rudder units mounted approximately one-third the way along the wings. The first of three XF7U-1 prototypes flew on 29 September 1948, followed by 14 F7U-1s for carrier evaluation and training duties from 1952, each powered by two Westinghouse J34-WE-32 turbojets. The next Cutlass, the 2087kg (4600lb) thrust J46-WE-8A-engined F7U-3, was the main production version, accounting for 180 of the 304 production fighters built. Larger than the F7U-1, it had folding wings and carried armament of four 20mm cannon and a pack of Mighty Mouse air-to-air rockets under the fuselage. Two further rocket packs or other weapons could be carried underwing for attack missions. Delivery of the F7U-3 began in 1954, followed by 12 photographic reconnaissance variants as F7U-3Ps. The last

production version of the Cutlass was the F7U-3M, basically the F7U-3 with provision for four Sparrow missiles. Maximum speed of the F7U-3 was 1094km/h (680mph). Despite its looks, the Cutlass was the US Navy's first production fighter capable of Mach 1, its first jet capable of delivering bombs at Mach 1, and its first jet capable of being catapult launched while armed with 2268kg (5000lb) of bombs for a strike mission.

Before merging with Ling-Temco Electronics, to form Ling-Temco-Vought in 1961, Chance Vought had in production its F-8 Crusader, a remarkable aircraft with a two-position adjustable-incidence high-mounted wing. By having the wing in its 'up' high angle-of-attack position, take off and landing speeds could be reduced while leaving the fuselage (and pilot's line of

Above: an LTV F-8E (FN) Crusader fighter of the French navy.

sight) level with the carrier deck. Designed to fulfil a US Navy requirement for a supersonic carrier-based air-superiority fighter, the first Crusader prototype flew for the first time on 25 March 1955. Altogether 1259 production Crusaders were built, including 42 exported to France (able to launch Matra R 530 and Sidewinder missiles) but not including modernized versions. Production for the US Navy began with the F-8A, the only version to have more than 300 built, which became operational in 1957. Powered by one Pratt & Whitney J57-P-12 or J57-P-4A turbojet, rated at 7257kg (16,000lb) thrust and 7327kg (16,200lb) thrust respectively, it was a day fighter only. A photographic reconnaissance sub-variant was the RF-8A. In the early 1980s, surviving F-8As were used as TF-8A trainers. The 'A' was followed by the J57-P-4A-powered F-8B, which featured an improved radar, and the F-8C day fighter with a 7665kg (16,900lb) thrust J57-P-16 engine and featuring two ventral fins.

The first limited all-weather version of the Crusader was the F-8D, powered by an 8165kg (18,000lb) thrust J57-P-20 engine. The F-8E became the second most numerous US Navy version, although, if the French Navy F-8E(FN)s are added, it actually outnumbered the F-8A. It was basically an improved F-8D with an enlarged radome. Armament of this version was four 20mm cannon plus four Sidewinder missiles carried on the fuselage, although later F-8Es were also given provision for heavy and medium bombs or rockets. Subsequent Crusaders were all modernized versions of earlier types and included the F-8H (used also by the Philippines), F-8J, F-8K and F-8L. Maximum speed of the F-8E was about 2127km/h (1322mph). In the early 1980s France still operated 25 F-8E(FN)s, the Philippines operated 24 F-8Hs as fighter-bombers, while the US Navy had surviving reconnaissance RF-8Gs only.

Prior to acquiring Crusaders, France had been one of a very small band of countries that had built fighters to serve on board its own carriers. SNCASE, which had built

Vampire fighters soon after the end of World War II, later also constructed under license slightly modified versions of the de Havilland Sea Venom under the type name Aquilon. All Aquilons were powered by Italian-built Ghost 48 Mk 1 turbojets, rated at 2200kg (4850lb) thrust, and standard armament was four 20mm cannon and eight rockets. The first Aquilon flew on 31 October 1952. Production began with 50 two-seat Mk 20s and Mk 202s, the latter only for use on board carriers. Delivery of the Mk 202s ended in the spring of 1956, when production began of 40 sea-going Mk 203 single-seaters, equipped with more advanced radar and capable of carrying two Matra 5103 air-to-air missiles. The only other version was the Mk 204 unarmed two-seat trainer, bringing the total number of Aquilons to 109. Maximum speed of the fighter was 960km/h (597mph).

The Aquilon was replaced on French aircraft carriers by the Crusader and the French-designed Dassault-Breguet Etendard IV-M, the carriers *Clemenceau* and *Foch* (commissioned in 1961 and 1963)

Above: a Dassault-Breguet Super Etendard pictured aboard a French aircraft carrier.

Left: Yakovlev Yak-36MP *Forger-As* aboard a *Kiev*-class carrier.

flown in production form on 24 November 1977, the Super Etendard is powered by one 5000kg (11,023lb) thrust SNECMA Atar 8K-50 turbojet. It also has improved high-lift devices, a sophisticated nav/attack integrated avionics system, increased range, and can receive and give in-flight refuelling. Armament combinations can include Magic air-to-air missiles, rocket pods, an Exocet anti-shipping missile, or four 400kg and two 250kg bombs. Like the Etendard IV-M, its maximum speed is about Mach 1. By May 1981 all but 20 of the 71 Super Etendards on order for the French Navy had been delivered. Fourteen were also ordered by Argentina in 1979.

A more recent advocate of the aircraft carrier has been the Soviet Union, which, during the 1970s launched its first two 40,000

carrying one flight of each type alongside Breguet Alizé anti-submarine aircraft. The Etendard had originally been designed as a strike-fighter for operation from land bases, but the only version to enter production was the modified Navy Etendard IV-M, which had flown as a prototype on 21 May 1958. Altogether 74 Etendard IV-Ms were built, equipping two operational units and a land-based training unit. Each was powered by one 4400kg (9700lb) SNECMA Atar 8B turbojet and carried two 30mm cannon, Sidewinder missiles or up to 1360kg (3000lb) of attack weapons. A reconnaissance and tanker version became the Etendard IV-P.

In 1973 the French Navy requested an improved Etendard to replace both the original version and the Crusader. First

Above: a de Havilland Sea Vixen F(AW). Mk. 2 all-weather fighter.

ton carrier/cruisers *Kiev* and *Minsk*. Far more akin to the new Royal Navy *Invincible* class of vessel than the huge US Navy carriers, these operate helicopters and the fairly new Yakovlev Yak-36MP (NATO *Forger-A*) single-seat VTOL combat aircraft. *Forger-A* uses a horizontally-installed main turbojet, exhausting through two vectoring nozzles to the rear of the wings and two vertically-mounted lift-jets. With a maximum speed of about Mach 1.1, *Forger-A* could have many uses, its two wing pylons being capable of carrying guns, air-to-air missiles, rocket packs and other stores. The NATO name *Forger-B* relates to a two-seat training variant.

Besides the United States, Britain has produced the greatest number of naval jet fighters. The Sea Vampire has already been mentioned. It was followed from the de Havilland stable by the D.H.112 Sea Venom, the naval version of the land-based Venom. Evolved as an all-weather fighter from the two-seat Venom NF.Mk.2, the Royal Navy first received 2200kg (4850lb) thrust de Havilland Ghost 103-powered F(AW). Mk. 20s and F(AW).Mk.21s, the latter with power-operated controls, special avionics, a power jettisonable cockpit hood and ejection seats. The F(AW).Mk.22, with a more-powerful Ghost 105 engine, followed. These served until 1960. The French also built Sea Venoms as Aquilons, while the Royal Australian Navy received a version of the F(AW).Mk.21 as the Mk.53.

De Havilland's D.H.110 two-seat all-weather day and night fighter followed the Sea Venom into Royal Navy service, having completed aircraft carrier trials in the spring of 1956. Powered by two Rolls-Royce Avon 208 turbojets mounted side-by-side in the rear of the fuselage nacelle, it followed de Havilland's predilection for the twin-boom configuration. The pilot occupied a cockpit offset to port, while the second crew member sat within the fuselage to starboard. Production of the Sea Vixen for the Royal Navy lasted until 1964, initially covering 119 F(AW). Mk.1s, each carrying 28 2in rockets on retractable underfuselage racks plus up to four Firestreak air-to-air missiles, or optionally various combinations of extra rockets, missiles and attack weapons. Twenty-nine longer-range F(AW).Mk.2s had Red Tops as their missile armament. Sea Vixens became operational from 1959.

Despite the many 'firsts' de Havilland jet fighters can claim, it was the Supermarine Attacker that became the first British standard single-seat carrier jet fighter. Originally conceived to use the Rolls-Royce Nene as an RAF fighter, it made use of the straight wings and tailwheel landing gear developed for the piston-engined Supermarine Spiteful/Seafang. The first Attacker flew on 27 July 1946 as an RAF prototype, but

Left: the de Havilland Sea Venom was a navalized version of the RAF's Venom night fighter.

Right: Supermarine Attacker F.Mk. 1s were the first standard, single-seat jet fighters in the Fleet Air Arm.

the following two prototypes conformed to Navy requirements. Carrier trials on board HMS *Illustrious* took place in 1947. The type entered service from 1951 in Attacker F.Mk.1 interceptor and then, from 1952, in Attacker FB.Mk.1 fighter-bomber versions, each with one 2313kg (5100lb) thrust Nene 3 turbojet in the fuselage. The later Attacker FB.Mk.2 used the Nene 102. The 61 Attacker Mk.1s for the Royal Navy were armed with four 20mm cannon plus two 1000lb bombs or several 60lb rockets underwing, while FB.MK.2s could carry up to 12 rockets in addition to the other weapons. Maximum speed of the FB.Mk.2 was 950km/h (590 mph). A further 36 Attacker F.Mk.1s were built, these serving with the Royal Pakistan Air Force.

Supermarine followed the Attacker with the Scimitar for the Royal Navy, a far more ambitious single-seat interceptor and strike aircraft. Powered by two 5103kg (11,250lb) thrust Avon Mk 202 turbojets, it became the Navy's first swept-wing jet when it entered service in 1958, initially operating from HMS *Victorious* in 1959. In total 76 Scimitars were built. Each was capable of a maximum speed of 1143km/h (710mph), and was armed as an interceptor with four 30mm Aden guns and optionally 96 air-to-air rockets or later four Sidewinder missiles.

Below: Hawker Sea Hawk Mk. 100s of the West German Navy operated from land bases.

Top: a Hawker Sea Hawk F(GA). Mk. 4 flies over St Michael's Mount on the Cornish coast.

Above: Supermarine Scimitar F. Mk. 1 strike fighters entered Fleet Air Arm service in 1958.

As a strike aircraft the Scimitar could carry air-to-surface missiles, conventional or tactical nuclear bombs, or rockets. Scimitars were retired from first-line service in 1965.

Perhaps the greatest early British success story in the naval jet fighter field was the Hawker (Armstrong Whitworth) Sea Hawk, a straight-winged single-seat fighter that entered service with the Royal Navy, Royal Netherlands Navy, Indian Navy (including ex Royal Navy and German Navy aircraft) and German Navy. It was finally to be found on board the Indian Navy carrier *Vikrant,* serving in an attack role into the early 1980s. Designed by Hawker Aircraft but manufactured from 1953 by Armstrong Whitworth, the Sea Hawk first flew as a prototype in 1947. The Royal Navy went on to receive 95 Sea Hawk F.Mk.1 and 40 F.MK.2 interceptors, 116 FB.Mk.3 fighter-bombers, and 183 F(GA) Mk.4 and 6 fighter-bombers, plus FB.MK.5s converted from Mk.3s. All these had Nene 101 engines except for the F(GA)Mk.6 and converted FB.Mk.5, which used Nene 104s and 103s respectively. Exports accounted for more than 100 aircraft. Maximum speed of the F(GA)Mk.6 was 964km/h (599mph). Armament for the Sea Hawk interceptors increased from four 20mm cannon alone to the use of rockets or

Above: a Sea Hawk F (GA). Mk. 6 ground attack fighter is shown with wings folded.

Left: a British Aerospace Sea Harrier FRS. Mk. 1 is armed with Sidewinder missiles.

Sidewinder missiles, while fighter-bombers could carry additionally 500lb bombs or other weapons.

The final aircraft described in this chapter is considered by many to represent a type of combat aircraft which will become ever more prominent as this century closes. It is the British BAe Sea Harrier, the naval counterpart of the highly-successful land-based Harrier. A V/STOL fighter, reconnaissance and strike aircraft, the Sea Harrier is now the Royal Navy's only fixed-wing combat jet and serves on board the *Invincible* class of anti-submarine cruisers. Powered by one 9752kg (21,500lb) thrust Rolls-Royce Pegasus Mk 104 vectored-thrust turbofan, it is thought to be more versatile than its Soviet counterpart, and has a maximum speed of Mach 1.25.

The first Sea Harrier flew initially on 20 August 1978 and sea trials on board HMS *Hermes* were first conducted in late 1979. Altogether the Royal Navy is expected to receive 34 aircraft, as Sea Harrier FRS.Mk. 1s, 15 serving with three front-line units on board the carriers. The Indian Navy has also ordered the Sea Harrier, its six aircraft receiving the British designation FRS.Mk.51. So-called 'ski-jump' launching ramps used on *Invincible* class vessels allow the Sea Harrier to take off at lower STOL speeds and carry heavier weapon loads, while the wide range of weapon options include Sidewinder air-to-air missiles, or air-to-surface missiles for Royal Navy aircraft and French R 550 Magic air-to-air missiles for Indian examples.

An advanced version of the Harrier for US Marine Corps (and RAF) use is also under development as the McDonnell Douglas AV-8B, which is expected to increase greatly the aircraft's weapon load and combat radius. Powered by a 9752kg (21,500lb) thrust Pegasus 11-21E engine, it is expected to achieve the required performance increases through changes to the airframe, including the use of a supercritical wing. At present only development aircraft are flying, and only time will tell if the USMC actually receives the 336 AV-8Bs it wants.

From Sea Hawk to Sea Harrier, Phantom to Tomcat, aviation history has shown that jet fighters for the navies flying from hazardous carrier decks have matched their land-based counterparts for performance time and time again, occasionally even surpassing them.

6: CENTURY FIGHTERS

The so-called Century Series of jet fighters covered six types operated by the USAF, with military designations from F-100 to F-106. These were most prominent during the 1950s and 1960s. Also covered in this chapter are the fighters from other nations that were contemporaries of this series.

The first Century Series fighter to fly in prototype form was the North American F-100 Super Sabre. Originating as a development of the Sabre, the first prototype flew on 25 May 1953, followed just five months later by the first production F-100A. This was a single-seat day fighter, powered by one 4400kg (9700lb) thrust Pratt & Whitney J57-P-7 or J57-P-39 turbojet installed in the rear fuselage. Armament comprised four 20mm cannon, plus underwing stores when

Right: a Convair F-102A Delta Dagger serving with a unit of the Air National Guard.

Overleaf: a North American F-100C Super Sabre broke the world air speed record in August 1955.

Above: the North American F-107A was an advanced Mach 2 development of the Super Sabre.

required. A photographic reconnaissance variant became the RF-100A. The first fighter-bomber, and next version was the F-100C, powered by a 7710kg (17,000lb) thrust J57-P-21A turbojet. The 'C' was given eight underwing hardpoints for up to 3402kg (7500lb) of weapons. Interestingly an F-100C broke the YF-100A prototype's world speed record on 20 August 1955 by achieving 1323km/h (822mph). This record was to last until March of the following year, when Britain easily gained the record with its Fairey Delta 2.

The major production version of the Super Sabre was the F-100D, similarly powered to the 'C' but incorporating many refinements, including an enlarged vertical tail. Armament comprised four 20mm cannon, plus four Sidewinder or air-to-air

Left: a North American QF-100D unpiloted target drone aircraft converted from an F-100D.

missiles or other weapons. In total 1274 F-100Ds were built. The only other version of the Super Sabre was the tandem two-seat F-100F operational trainer. USAF F-100s were flown in Vietnam, but the last were recently retired. However Super Sabres were supplied to other nations under MDAP and a few still fly in Turkey and Taiwan. Maximum speed of the F-100D is 1390km/h (864mph). It is worth mentioning that an experimental development of the F-100 was the F-107A, three being built as Mach 2 plus advanced fighter-bomber prototypes, with bifurcated air intakes above the fuselage and J75 engines.

Chronologically the next of the Series was the Convair F-102 Delta Dagger, which first flew in prototype form on 24 October 1953. it was the first of Convair's combat jets to use delta shaped wings, as flown on the experimental XF-92A, and 875 production F-102As were built from 1956. As with the TF-102A two-seat training version, power was provided by a single 7800kg (17,200lb) thrust (with afterburning) Pratt & Whitney J57-P-23 or J57-P-25 turbojet. Armament comprised one AIM-26B and three AIM-4C Falcon air-to-air missiles, carried internally. Delta Daggers served for many years with Air Defense Command, but by the end of

the 1970s even those passed to the Turkish Air Force had been retired. Maximum speed was 1327km/h (825mph).

From the Delta Dagger Convair developed the F-106 Delta Dart, powered by a 11,113kg (24,500lb) thrust Pratt & Whitney J57-P-17 turbojet to give a maximum speed of 2455km/h (1525mph). A total of 227 single-seat F-106A interceptors was built for Air Defense Command, the first flying on 26 December 1956, plus a number of F-106B two-seat trainers. Outwardly the F-106A could easily be identified from the F-102A by its redesigned straight-topped vertical tail and side air intakes which ended just forward of the wing leading-edges. Originally armed with one Genie or Super Genie unguided air-to-air missile and four Super Falcon missiles, many aircraft were later given a 20mm cannon. In the early 1980s the USAF still operated about 223 Delta Darts.

First flown on 7 February 1954, the Lockheed F-104 Starfighter was the third Century Series jet. However, it was destined not to enjoy the success of the other fighters with the USAF, although eventually Starfighters were to be operated by 14 other nations. Featuring a long pointed fuselage, accommodating a large turbojet engine and very short-span thin straight wings, the Star-

Above: the first Convair F-106A Delta Dart interceptor for the USAF's Air Defense Command.

Left: Lockheed F-104G Starfighters of West Germany's Luftwaffe fly in formation.

Right: this view of a Convair F-106A accentuates the type's 'area ruled' fuselage.

fighter followed closely the general arrangement of the Douglas X-3 research aircraft (flown in 1952). This configuration ensured a Mach 2 capability, but was also partly the cause of the numerous accidents that befell the fighter. However some pilots have considered the Starfighter one of the best jet fighters ever built and a 'homebuilt' privately reconstructed F-104 currently holds the world low-altitude speed record.

Early production Starfighters were split between Air Defense Command and Tactical Air Command (and exported in small numbers), the former receiving 179 F-104A single-seaters and F-104B two-seaters and the latter 98 similar F-104Cs and F-104Ds. However it took the F-104G multi-mission version to get the fighter really established,

Below: three Lockheed F-104 Starfighters of the United States Air Force fly in formation.

powered by a 7167kg (15,800lb) thrust (with afterburning) General Electric J79-GE-11A turbojet. This became a European version, being built under license in Belgium, Germany, the Netherlands and Italy, covering more than 1000 aircraft. Other production lines were set up in Canada and Japan, as well as in the United States, and other recipient nations included Denmark, Greece, Norway, Spain and Turkey. The two-seat variant was the TF-104G.

The USAF no longer operates Starfighters and those of Belgium, Denmark, the Netherlands and Norway are being replaced by General Dynamics F-16s. German and Italian F-104Gs are being retired also with the introduction of the Panavia Tornado. But Italy also license-built the final version of the Starfighter, the F-104S. Following Lockheed-built prototypes, Aeritalia produced 248 F-104Ss by 1979, entering Italian Air Force service from 1969 and 40 going to

Turkey. This uprated version of the 'G' is powered by an 8120kg (17,900lb) thrust (with afterburning) J79-GE-19 turbojet. It has a maximum speed of 2330km/h (1450mph) and carries a 20mm rotary cannon plus two Sparrow and two Sidewinder air-to-air missiles, although a wide range of other weapons can be carried on its nine stores attachment points.

Flying just after the Starfighter was McDonnell's F-101 Voodoo, a single or two-seat long-range interceptor and reconnaissance aircraft. As mentioned earlier, in mid-1946 McDonnell began the design of an experimental long-range penetration fighter as the XF-88. This first flew in October 1948. In 1950 further development of the XF-88 was cancelled, but in the following year the program was revived, producing the F-101. The first Voodoo flew on 29 September 1954. Tactical Air Command received 124 single-seat F-101As and F-

Top left: three McDonnell Voodoos fly together, with an F-101A in the foreground.

Top: the two-seat F-101B Voodoo was a two-seat interceptor for Air Defense Command.

Left: the ultimate version of the Lockheed Starfighter is the Italian-built F-104S.

Above: Republic F-105 Thunderchief fighter-bombers.

Right: a Mikoyan MiG-17 of the Egyptian air force.

Overleaf: Chinese Shenyang J-6s operating at night.

101Cs, the latter suitable for low-level attack duties and with provision for carrying a tactical nuclear weapon. In 1957 the F-101B tandem two-seat all-weather interceptor flew for Air Defense Command. With TF-101B trainers, a total of 480 'Bs' was built. From 1967 some F-101A/Cs were converted into reconnaissance RF-101G/Hs for reserve units. Ex-USAF F-101Bs and trainers were also acquired by Canada, which still operated 62 at the beginning of the 1980s, although these are to be replaced by Hornets. Powered by two 6750kg (14,880lb) thrust (with afterburning) Pratt & Whitney J57-P-55 turbojets, the F-101B has a maximum speed of 1963km/h (1220mph) and is armed with two Genie unguided missiles and three Falcon missiles.

The last of the Century Series to enter production was the F-105 Thunderchief, Republic's last 'Thunder' jet. The first prototype flew on 22 October 1955 and the first 75

production single-seat tactical fighter-bombers were designated F-105Bs. These were each powered by one Pratt & Whitney J75-P-3 or J75-P-5 turbojet engine. The main production version was the F-105D, an all-weather fighter-bomber powered by one 12,030kg (26,500lb) thrust (with afterburning) J75-P-19W turbojet. This possesses a maximum speed of 2230km/h (1385mph).

Six hundred F-105Ds were built, one of the versions that make up the 180 or so Thunderchiefs still flown by the USAF. As well as having a 20mm multi-barrel cannon in the nose, it can be armed with more than 6350kg (14,000lb) of externally-carried weapons, the wide range of stores including 3000lb conventional or nuclear bombs and four Sidewinder missiles. A small number of F-105Ds were modified to carry the T-Stick II bombing system.

First flown in 1963, the F-105F was de-

veloped as an operational two-seat trainer. Featuring a longer fuselage, an increased gross weight of 24,495kg (54,000lb) and a taller fin and rudder, the F-105F was, like the F-105D, flown widely in Vietnam. Altogether 143 'Fs' were built, a number of which were later converted into ground defense suppression aircraft for use in Vietnam, designated F-105G. The 'G' itself was the final Thunderchief variant and featured an ECM pod and four Shrike or Standard ARM air-to-surface anti-radiation missiles, enabling the aircraft to attack anti-aircraft

missile sites, a role increasingly important to the US forces in Vietnam as its air offensive gathered pace. However the Thunderchief was only one of several types of aircraft that used these missiles operationally.

Like the United States, the Soviet Union developed several new fighters during the 1950s, probably the most important of which was the Mikoyan MiG-21. However to supersede the MiG-15 on production lines, a new fighter was developed as the MiG-17. This began life as little more than a refined MiG-15, the main changes being made to the rear fuselage and tail unit to improve handling characteristics at high speed. Slightly longer than the earlier fighter, the first version received the NATO name *Fresco-A*. It was a single-seat interceptor powered by a 2700kg (5952lb) thrust VK-1 turbojet, entering service in 1953. Slight changes produced the MiG-17P (NATO *Fresco-B*), most easily identified by the

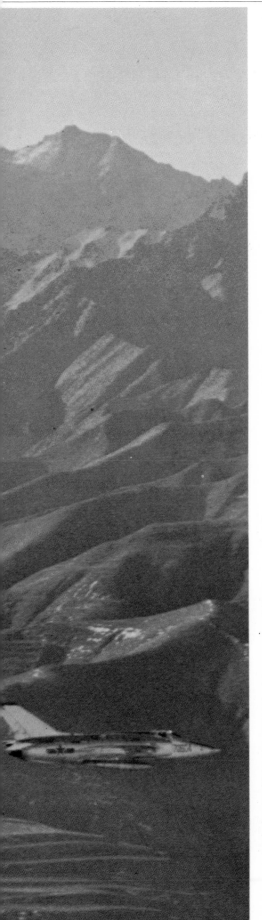

more forward position of its dive brakes. The MiG-17F (NATO *Fresco-C*) was the major production day fighter, powered by a 3380kg (7451lb) thrust VK-1A turbojet, allowing a maximum speed of 1145km/h (711mph). Armament later changed from the usual single 37mm N-37 cannon and two 23mm NR-23 cannon to three NR-23s, while beneath the wings could be carried rocket pods or 500kg (1102lb) of bombs. Limited all-weather interceptor capability came with the MiG-17PF (*Fresco-D*), which carried an improved radar in the nose. When AA-1 (*Alkali*) first generation air-to-air missiles became available, with a range of 6 to 8km (3.75 to 5 miles), a non-afterburning version of the MiG-17PF, known to NATO as *Fresco-E,* became a carrier for four. Production of the MiG-17 went on into the early 1960s, with manufacture under licence being undertaken also in Czechoslovakia, Poland and China. MiG-17s remain flying with a great many air forces, the Air Force of the People's Liberation Army (China) and the People's Navy still operating more than 1000 and several hundred respectively under the Chinese designations Shenyang J-5 (MiG-17F) and J-5A (MiG-17PF).

Soon after early MiG-17s began to appear, Mikoyan flew its MiG-19 prototype, a Mikulin AM-5-engined fighter first flown on 18 September 1953. The MiG-19 was the Soviet equivalent of the early US Century Series fighters and the British Hunter, entering service with the air defense force from 1955. The first production version attained Mach 1.1 performance on the power of two 3040kg (6702lb) thrust AM-5F turbojets, later reengined as the MiG-19F with Tumansky R-9BFs. Several other versions were produced as day and limited all-weather fighters and fighter-bombers, armed normally with one 37mm N-37 and two 23mm NR-23 cannon plus bombs and rockets for ground attack, although on the MiG-19PM four *Alkali* missiles were introduced.

Known to NATO as *Farmer,* the Soviet-built MiG-19 is currently only operated by Cuba, although Chinese-built MiG-19s serve with several air forces. It was superseded on Soviet production lines in 1958, but manufacture in China under the Shenyang J-6 designation has kept the aircraft in production. The original Chinese version was the MiG-19S, a three 30mm NR-30 cannon-firing and rocket/bomb-carrying day fighter powered by two 3300kg (7275lb) thrust (with afterburning) R-9B turbojets. This first entered service in 1962. Today the Chinese air force and navy operate an estimated 2000 MiG-19s of various models for interceptor, ground attack and reconnaissance duties.

The Nanzhang Q-5 is a Chinese fighter-bomber, that nation's first high-performance combat plane of indigenous development and manufacture, although loosely

Left: a formation of Chinese Nanzhang Q-5 fighter-bombers fly over typical terrain.

Above: a Soviet-built Mikoyan MiG-19 pictured in service with the Egyptian air force.

based on the MiG. Armament comprises two 30mm cannon, four 250kg bombs carried internally, a similar number of bombs carried externally or other stores. Maximum speed has been estimated at Mach 1.35. Known to NATO as *Fantan-A,* Q-5s entered Chinese air force and navy service in the late 1970s and have been exported to Pakistan.

Equivalent to the later US Century Series fighters, three of four single-engined Soviet fighters that appeared in prototype form during 1955-56 were the Mikoyan MiG-21, Sukhoi Su-7 and Su-9. The prototype Su-7, designated S-1, first flew in 1955 as a single-seat ground attack fighter. Preproduction aircraft were known as Su-7s, but production aircraft proper were ordered in 1958 as Su-7Bs. Considerably heavier than the MiG, the Su-7B differs further from this and the Su-9 by having sweptback wings. Several versions have appeared over the years, the Su-7BMK being one of the most important because of its ability to be operated from short and unprepared airfields. To do this it has a low pressure nosewheel tyre and can be fitted with JATO. Powered by a 10,000kg (22,046lb) thrust (with afterburning) Lyulka AL-7F-1 turbojet, allowing a maximum speed of Mach 1.6, the aircraft can carry two 750kg and two 500kg bombs or rockets in addition to its fixed pair of 30mm cannon. Known to NATO as *Fitter-A,* the Su-7B is still in service with the Soviet and other air forces.

The Su-9, which appeared about the same time as the Su-7, was designed as a single-seat all-weather fighter, entering service in the Soviet Union in 1959. Known to NATO as *Fishpot-B,* the Su-9 has delta wings and carries four *Alkali* air-to-air missiles. Power is provided by a 9000kg (19,842lb) thrust (with afterburning) AL-7F engine. The Su-9 remains in the Soviet inventory, as does a refined version known as the Su-11, which has been given the reporting name *Fishpot-C* by NATO. The Su-11 has a longer nose with less taper, housing an improved radar and is powered by an AL-7F-1 engine. Carrying two *Anab* air-to-air missiles and a drop-tank, it has a maximum speed of about Mach 1.2, although this increases to Mach 1.8 without external

Above right: the Soviet MiG-21 is the most widely used combat aircraft in the world.

Right: a Soviet Sukhoi Su-7B ground-attack fighter pictured in Egyptian air force service.

stores. It too remains in use today.

The third of the 1955-56 fighters was the MiG-21. Proving to be the most successful in terms of longevity of production and with the greatest development potential, it is the lightest in weight by far. With high-speed, a good rate of climb and maneuverability, and good handling characteristics as the aim, the MiG-21 prototype first flew on 16 June 1956 as the E-5. Just over a week later it took part in an air display over Moscow. It entered production initially as a day fighter only, armed with two 30mm cannon. Power was provided by a 5100kg (11,244lb) thrust (with afterburning) Tumansky R-11 turbojet and this became known to NATO as *Fishbed-A*.

Fishbed-A was very quickly superseded in production by the slightly more powerful MiG-21F (*Fishbed-C*), also built in Czechoslovakia and armed with one cannon and two *Atoll* air-to-air missiles or rockets. The MiG-21PF (*Fishbed-D*) introduced limited all-weather capability, so matching the Sukhois for the first time, while the MiG-21PFMA (*Fishbed-J*) was developed as a multi-role version armed with a 23mm GSh-23 gun and carrying two *Atoll* and two *Advanced Atoll* missiles or four *Advanced Atolls*, rockets, bombs, air-to-surface missiles or other weapons. Many other versions of the MiG-21 have been built for the Soviet air force and for export to many countries, including third-generation types, reconnaissance models and two-seat trainers. The MiG-21 has become the world's most used fighter and about one-quarter of all Soviet tactical fighters are of this type. The most powerful version is the MiG-21bis (*Fishbed-N*) multi-role version, powered by a 7500kg (16,535lb) thrust (with afterburning) Tumansky R-25 turbojet, giving it the Mach 2 plus performance of the developed versions. In addition to using Soviet supplied MiG-21s, China also produced a small number during the mid-1960s as Xian J-7s.

Back in 1953 the prototype of the Soviet Union's first twin-engined all-weather fighter appeared, subsequently entering production as the Yak-25 (NATO *Flashlight*). A two-seater, it had subsonic performance on the power of two underwing-mounted AM-5 or RD-9 turbojets and was armed with two 37mm cannon and an underfuselage pack of air-to-air rockets. A small number of refined Yak-27s (also

Left: MiG-21 fighters of the Egyptian air force have seen action against the Israelis.

Bottom: a Dassault Mystère IIC serving with the French Air Force's 10e Escadre.

Below: a Mirage F1 leads a Mirage III two-seater, Super Mystère and Mystère IVA.

Right: a Sud Aviation SO 4050 Vautour II-N two-seat fighter taxies to the runway.

Flashlight) with pointed noses, increased wing spans and engines with afterburners, was also produced.

Although *Flashlight* went out of service years ago, its replacement as a two-seat twin-engined all-weather fighter that ap-

Right: the Vautour II-A was a single-seat fighter bomber version of the Sud-Aviation SO 4050.

Below: the Dassault Mirage III-A prototype was an early example of the famous Mirage III series.

peared during the early 1960s as the Yak-28P (NATO *Firebar*) is still used. Just one of the production versions of the Yak-28, which included attack aircraft known to NATO as *Brewers,* about 300 *Firebars* remain with the Soviet air force today as home defense interceptors. Carrying two *Anab* missiles, *Firebar* has Mach 1.1 performance on the power of two 5950kg (13,117lb) thrust Tumansky R-11 engines fitted below the swept wings. Another older aircraft used as a home defense type is the Tupolev Tu-28P (NATO *Fiddler*), which entered service during the 1960s and about

130 remain in use. The largest fighter ever used operationally, it is a two-seater powered by two rear-fuselage-mounted 12,250kg (27,000lb) thrust (with afterburning) turbojets, bestowing a maximum speed of 1850km/h (1150mph). Armament comprises four *Ash* air-to-air missiles.

France kept up the momentum set by its Dassault Ouragan by putting four new fighters into service during the 1950s. The first was the Dassault Mystère, flown as a prototype on 23 February 1951. The Nene or Tay-powered prototypes were followed by Mystère IICs with SNECMA Atar 101 en-

gines, mainly for the French air force. The IIC was followed into production by the Mystère IVA, of which 421 were produced with Tay and 3500kg (7716lb) thrust Hispano-Suiza Verdon 350 turbojets, most with the Verdon. The majority went into French service, although India and Israel received reasonable numbers. Maximum speed was 1100km/h (684mph). A handful of Mystère IVBs were also built with new radar and afterburners. No Mystères remain in operational use today.

From the Mystère was developed the Super-Mystère B-2, the first production air-

craft flying in 1957. Most of the 180 built went to the French air force, although Israel received a few. Powered by the 4400kg (9700lb) thrust Atar 101G turbojet engine, maximum speed was 1195km/h (743mph). Armament comprised two 30mm DEFA cannon and a pack of air-to-air rockets, plus ground attack or air-to-air missiles under

Left: the Dassault Mirage III-B was a tandem two-seat training variant of the Mirage III fighter.

Below: a line-up of Mirage III-C interceptors of France's Armée de l'Air.

the wings. The last in service were 12 ex-Israeli Pratt & Whitney J52-powered B-2s refurbished and delivered to Honduras in 1977.

The third French fighter was one of three combat versions of the Sud-Aviation SO 4050 Vautour, 70 of which were built as Vautour II-N two-seat all-weather fighters. First flown on 10 October 1956, the II-N was powered by two underwing 3500kg (7716lb) thrust Atar 101E-3s, giving it a maximum speed of 1100km/h (684mph). Armament was made up of four 30mm DEFA cannon, plus many rockets or four Matra R 511 missiles.

By far the most important of the French fighters that first appeared in the 1950s was the Dassault Mirage III, which first flew on 17 November 1956 as a single-seat all-weather prototype fighter capable of operating from short and unprepared airfields. The Mirage III remains in production today, making up the majority of the 1336 Mirage IIIs/5s/50s delivered to the French and twenty other air forces by March 1981.

The single 6000kg (13,228lb) thrust Atar 9B turbojet engine replaced the earlier-used Atar 101G for the Mirage III-A and III-C production aircraft, of which 10 and 95 were built respectively for French opera-

Above: a Mirage III-RD tactical reconnaissance aircraft of the French air force.

Left: Dassault Mirage 5 fighters bought by Saudi Arabia for later transfer to Egypt.

Top right: the Mirage III-EL was an export version of the III-E for the Lebanese air force.

Above right: the Mirage 50 is a multimission fighter intended for export, which first flew in 1979.

Right: the Saab J 32B Lansen was an all-weather interceptor fighter for the Swedish air force.

tion. Other Mirage III-Cs were delivered to Israel, South Africa and Switzerland. Versions currently available are the Mirage III-D two-seat operational trainer, Mirage III-E long-range fighter-bomber and intruder variant, and the Mirage III-R reconnaissance variant. The III-E is the most important of these, gaining its Mach 2.2 performance from its single 6200kg (13,669lb) thrust (with afterburning) Atar 9C engine. A total of 523 have been built, delivered from 1964, which include two squadrons in French ser-

vice equipped to carry tactical nuclear weapons. Normal armament for interceptor duties is one Matra R 530 and two Sidewinder air-to-air missiles or the R 530 and guns.

The Mirage III introduced Dassault's now common use of low-mounted delta wings and a vertical tail only, as later fitted to the Mirage 5 ground attack development of the III-E, that was first flown in 1967, and the Mirage 50 multi-mission fighter. The Mirage 50 was first flown in 1979. Production air-

craft have been delivered to Chile, with the 7200kg (15,873lb) thrust (with afterburning) Atar 9K-50 engine fitted. The latest Mirages also use delta wings, as described in the last chapter.

In Sweden during the 1950s, Saab continued its tradition of supplying that nation's air force with fighters, by following the Saab-29 with the Saab-32 Lansen. This was a completely new swept-wing combat plane, designed to the requirements as laid down by the Swedish air force and including the

Above: a Saab J 35 Draken fighter of the Swedish air force is armed with Hughes Falcon missiles.

ability to operate from major roads in an emergency. First flown on 3 November 1952, it was eventually produced in A 32A all-weather attack, J 32B all-weather fighter and night-fighter, and S 32C photographic reconnaissance versions. The J 32B was powered by one 6900kg (15,200lb) thrust (with afterburning) Rolls-Royce R.M.6B (Avon 200) engine built in Sweden, and carried 30mm cannon plus four Sidewinder missiles or rockets. Seven Swedish squadrons flew J 32Bs from 1959. By the 1980s

Lansens served only in S 32C and converted J 32D target-towing and J 32E ECM versions.

The Lansen was followed quickly by the Saab-35 Draken, a Mach 2 fighter and reconnaissance aircraft. First flown on 25 October 1955, it was given a unique double-delta wing and single vertical tail, as previously flight tested on the reduced-scale Saab-210 research aircraft. The first production version was the J 35A interceptor, which entered Swedish air force service in 1960 powered by an R.M.6B engine. This

version is no longer flown. Some were converted to Sk 35C two-seat trainer standard and others to J 35Bs, the latter an improved interceptor with a collision-course fire-control system and electronic equipment compatible with Sweden's semi-automatic air defense system. Later interceptor versions were the J 35D, with an R.M.6C (Avon 300) engine, the J 35F major production version armed with one 30mm Aden cannon and four Saab-built US-designed HM-55 and HM-58 Falcon air-to-air missiles, and the

Saab-35X export Drakens, delivered to Finland and Denmark. Those for Finland can carry two cannon, up to four Sidewinders, air-to-air rockets or ground attack weapons. With the advent of the Viggen, Swedish Drakens currently operate only as S 35E reconnaissance aircraft and Sk 35C trainers.

The first of Britain's '1950s' fighters, although flown as a prototype in September 1949, was the de Havilland Venom. Its configuration was like the earlier Vampire, but it represented a much improved design and entered RAF service from 1952 in FB.Mk 1 and Mk.4 single-seat fighter-bomber and NF.Mk.2 and Mk.3 two-seat night-fighter versions. Power was provided by the de Havilland Ghost turbojet, giving the FB.Mk.1 a maximum speed of 1030km/h (640mph). Fixed armament comprised four 20mm cannon. Nearly 700 were built for the RAF and FB.Mk.50s were built under license in Switzerland. British Venoms were replaced by Hunters and Javelins.

The Hawker Hunter itself was a beautifully styled swept-wing fighter, powered by a single rear-mounted Avon turbojet. It first flew as a prototype on 20 July 1951, having been evolved via the experimental swept-wing version of the Sea Hawk, known as the P.1052, continuing Sydney Camm's belief that an aircraft should not only fly right but also look right. Even the Hunter's air brake was not allowed to spoil the lines, being fitted beneath the fuselage. Production Hunter F.Mk.1s entered service with the RAF from July 1954, these being powered by 3400kg (7500lb) thrust Avon 104 or 107

Right: the Hawker Hunter F. Mk. 1 entered service with RAF Fighter Command in 1954.

Below: a D.H. Venom FB.Mk.50 of the Swiss air force, which is the last operator of this fighter.

engines, the first F.Mk.1 off the production line having flown on 30 November 1952. Simultaneous production of the Armstrong Whitworth Sapphire Mk 101-powered Hunter F.Mk.2 took place at Armstrong Whitworth, but few were built. Only a single F.Mk.3 was produced by a conversion, and this took the world speed record from the US F-86D Sabre on 7 September 1953 by attaining an average speed of 1171km/h (727mph).

The Hunter F.Mk.4 was basically an improved F.Mk.1, powered by the Avon 115 on most aircraft. It also introduced underwing attachment points for drop-tanks or weapons to supplement the four 30mm Aden cannon. The Sapphire-powered F.Mk.5 was structurally improved, as was the F.Mk.4, while the more-powerful F.Mk.6 had the 4536kg (10,000lb) thrust Avon 203 engine. Later production F.Mk 6s.had extended leading-edge panels and the option of four underwing stores pylons. It entered

RAF service in 1956, becoming the standard RAF day fighter in Europe.

Of the 1985 Hunters built, many were two-seat trainers and F(GA) ground-attack variants. Production included Hunters built under license in Holland and Belgium, with others being exported to 14 countries in new or refurbished form. Today Hunters in service include 140 F.Mk.58 fighter-bombers operated by Switzerland. Maximum speed of the F.Mk.4 was Mach 0.9, making it undoubtedly the ultimate development of the subsonic fighter.

Hawker later became responsible for the lightweight British Gnat, a Mach 0.98 fighter armed with two cannon (plus rockets or bombs) developed by Folland Aircraft. It first flew on 18 July 1955. Production single-seaters, powered by one 2050kg (4520lb) thrust Bristol Siddeley Orpheus 701 turbojet

Below: a Folland Gnat lightweight fighter in service with the Finnish air force.

Below: a Hawker Hunter F(GA).Mk.9
ground attack fighter of No 45 Squadron,
Royal Air Force.

each, were not used by the RAF but were exported to Finland, India and Yugoslavia in small numbers. However the two-seat training variant later became well known to aviation enthusiasts all round the world as the mount of the RAF Red Arrows aerobatic team. A version of the Gnat has also been in production in India since about 1976 as the Ajeet (Invincible) interceptor and ground attack aircraft, as well as in two-seat training form, with 50 single-seaters built by HAL (Hindustan Aeronautics Ltd) by 1981.

Probably the least successful jet fighter produced in Britain for the RAF was the Supermarine Swift, which first flew as an Avon-powered prototype in August 1951. A contemporary of the Hunter, small numbers entered RAF service from 1953 to become that force's first swept-wing fighter, each armed with two or four 30mm cannon, but

Above: the Gloster Javelin F(AW).Mk.1 was the first RAF aircraft to be designed as an all-weather fighter.

Below: the first prototype Gloster Javelin was flown with the second cockpit covered over.

Right: the English Electric P.1A was developed into the Lightning by way of the P.1B.

were withdrawn during 1955. Only the Swift FR.Mk.5 fighter-reconnaissance version was successful, 60 serving between 1956 and 1961. The later Swift F.Mk.7 was used only in very small numbers as a test-bed for missiles.

Gloster Aircraft's only other successful production jet fighter after the Meteor was the Javelin, which was the world's first twin-engined delta-winged aircraft and the RAF's first purpose-designed all-weather fighter. The first of five prototypes flew on 26 November 1951 and RAF Fighter Command began operating production F(AW).Mk.1s in 1956. This first version was powered by two 3765kg (8300lb) thrust Sapphire ASSa.6 turbojets and carried four 30mm Aden guns. Like all nine versions of the Javelin, the F(AW).Mk.1 was a two-seater. Later versions were the F(AW).Mk.2, with an American-designed radar and equipment changes (first flown on 31 October 1955); the F(AW).Mk.4, with an all-moving horizontal tail (first flown 19 Sep-

Above: the Supermarine Swift F.Mk.7 was used to develop the Fairey Fireflash air-to-air missile.

tember 1955); the F(AW).Mk.5, with redesigned wings carrying more fuel (first flown 26 July 1956); the F(AW).Mk.6, with American radar (first flown 14 December 1956); the F(AW).Mk.7, major production version with Sapphire ASSa.7 engines, rated at 4990kg (11,000lb) thrust, airframe modifications, and the ability to carry four Firestreak air-to-air missiles and two guns (first flown 27 April 1956); and the final F(AW).Mk.8, with missiles, guns and afterburning engines (first flown 9 May 1958). In addition, most of the F(AW).Mk.7s were later modified to have afterburning and flight refuelling as Mk.9s. The last of about 400 Javelins were retired in 1967. Maximum speed of the F(AW).Mk.9 was 998km/h (620mph).

The final fighter in this chapter is, like several of the others, still in first-line use today. It is the BAC Lightning, originally the

English Electric Lightning. On 4 August 1954 the first of two English Electric P.1A flying prototypes took off, powered by two Sapphire engines. Designed to an Air Ministry specification for a manned supersonic research aircraft, it had its engines rearmounted one above the other, fed with air from a very large nose intake. From the P.1A was developed the refined P.1B. Like the earlier aircraft it had heavily-swept wings, but power was now provided by afterburning Avon turbojets. Also, the air

Left: an RAF BAC Lightning F.Mk.6 formates on a Handley Page Victor tanker aircraft.

Below: the Royal Saudi Air Force operates a version of the Lightning with ground attack capability.

intake featured a center-body or shock-cone. A P.1B first flew on 4 April 1957 and was the prototype to the Lightning F.Mk 1 and F.Mk 1A, powered by Avon 201s. Forty-eight Mk 1 types were built, able to launch Firestreak missiles, none of which remain in use. The use of Avon 210 engines with improved afterburners and the provision for Firestreak or Red Top missiles (in addition to the 30mm Aden guns) gave rise to the F.Mk 2 and modified 2A, neither of which remain in use.

The F.Mk 3 and 3A were provided with 7420kg (16360lb) thrust Avon 301 engines, missile armament only, redesigned vertical tails with angular tops, and reduced outer wing panel sweep (F.Mk 3A only). The RAF retains 19 today. Other than side-by-side two-seat trainers, the RAF received one more version only, as the F.Mk 6. First flown

in 1964, this version is basically a developed F.Mk 3 with increased fuel capacity. Armament comprise two missiles or two rocket packs, plus two 30mm Aden guns optionally. Most of the F.Mk 3/3As were converted to this standard. The RAF currently operates 40 F.Mk 6s, plus trainers. Two RAF squadrons operate Lightnings as home defense fighters, although Phantom IIs have recently taken over the major share of this role. Nevertheless the Lightning remains one of the fastest climbing fighters in the world, and has a maximum speed of more than Mach 2. But its high performance was not enough to win major export orders. Development had taken too long for this. Only Kuwait and Saudi Arabia purchased new and ex-RAF Lightnings, the Royal Saudi Air Force still operating 30 fighters and seven trainers in the 1980s.

7: INTO THE '80s

Many of the fighters covered in chapters five and six remain in use today. Some are even in production. But this chapter contains the fastest, highest climbing and most potent fighters ever built, as well as those of lesser ability. Interestingly the fastest military aircraft in service today is not a fighter but the Lockheed SR-71A strategic reconnaissance aircraft. Three of the original prototypes of the SR-71A were modified into experimental Mach 3 plus interceptors, being evaluated in 1964.

In the early 1980s the majority of fighters and fighter-bombers in USAF service were two-seat McDonnell Douglas F-4 Phantom IIs, the naval counterparts having already been described in chapter five. A total of more than 1700 was then listed. USAF interest in the Phantom II came about when trials in 1961 proved the aircraft to be well suited to ground attack in addition to fighter duties. The USAF's Tactical Air Command, Pacific Air Forces and United States Air Forces in Europe received the F-4C, which was based on the Navy/USMC F-4B, and powered by two General Electric J79-GE-15 turbojets. Some were later modified into

EF-4Cs, a version developed to carry ECM sensors and anti-radiation missiles to attack antiaircraft radar sites. Other so-called 'Wild Weasel' versions have included the EF-4D and F-4G Advanced Wild Weasel.

The USAF's F-4D was basically similar to the F-4C, but with improved avionics, while the F-4E provided multi-role capability. Delivered from October 1968, the 'E' has 8120kg (17,900lb) thrust J79-GE-17 engines, increased fuel capacity, and carries a fixed 20mm multi-barrel gun. Under MAP, F-4Es also went to Germany, Greece, Iran, Israel, Japan, South Korea, and Turkey. Others now

Overleaf: a General Dynamics F-16A Fighting Falcon.

Far left: the Lockheed YF-12A Mach 3 interceptor did not go into production.

Left: the 5000th Phantom built in the United States was an F-4E, which was delivered to Turkey.

Below: the McDonnell Douglas F-4E was the first variant of the Phantom to have built-in gun armament.

serve also with Australia and Egypt. In addition Mitsubishi of Japan has built 127 under license for the JASDF as F-4EJs, capable of carrying Mitsubishi AAM-2 missiles.

The F-4F fighter was produced for the German Luftwaffe, while the F-4M was the RAF version, a Rolls-Royce Spey-powered variant similar to the Royal Navy F-4K and also capable of carrying Sky Flash air-to-air missiles. The RAF received 118 from 1968. All Phantom II land-based versions remain operational today, except for the EF-4D, which can be regarded as a prototype version for the F-4G. Maximum speed of the F-4E is more than Mach 2, and air-to-air armament comprises the gun plus Sparrow or Sidewinder missiles.

The latest USAF fighter from McDonnell Douglas is the F-15 Eagle. Certainly one of the finest air superiority fighters in the world, it still retains ground attack capability. The single-seat F-15A Eagle was first flown on 27 July 1972, followed by the F-15B two-seat trainer on 7 July 1973. Unlike the contemporary US Navy Tomcat, the Eagle has fixed wings, but shares the relatively new concept of having twin fins and rudders. Powered by two 10,854kg (23,930lb) thrust (with afterburning) Pratt & Whitney F100-PW-100 turbofan engines, it has a maximum speed of more than Mach 2.5. Armament in the air superiority role comprises a 20mm multi-barrel gun plus four Sidewinders and four Sparrows.

By early 1981 600 Eagles had been delivered, those from mid-1979 as F-15Cs and F-15Ds (single and two-seaters respectively) to acknowledge the latest increase in fuel capacity and ability to carry low-drag external fuel and sensor pallets known as FAST Packs. The Packs attach to the sides of the air intakes and so do not detract from the aircraft's streamlining. The USAF plans

Above: a McDonnell Douglas F-15A Eagle air superiority fighter is pictured during a test flight.

Above right: an F-15C Eagle of the USAF's 36th Tactical Fighter Wing based at Bitburg, West Germany.

Right: an RAF Phantom FGR.Mk.2 is armed with Sparrow air-to-air missiles and bombs.

to receive 749 Eagles by 1983, while Israel has acquired 25 of an expected total of 40, Japan has received 14 from the United States and plans to build a further 86 under license as F-15Js and F-15DJs and deliveries of 60 Eagles to Saudi Arabia has begun. The name Strike Eagle refers to a specially developed ground attack version.

In an attempt to acquire a low-cost and lightweight supersonic fighter, mainly for overseas use under MAP, the US Department of Defense funded the production of the Northrop F-5A single-seat tactical fighter and two-seat operational F-5B, plus a photographic reconnaissance version. Many air forces received these under MAP or by purchase from the early 1960s. The F-5A attains a speed of 1488km/h (925mph) on the power of two 1850kg (4080lb) thrust (with afterburning) General Electric J85-GE-13 turbojets. Armament comprises two 20mm guns and two Sidewinders, plus underfuselage and underwing stores.

Northrop developed the F-5E and F-5F Tiger II to succeed the F-5A and F-5B. Increased maneuverability was the main aim for the Tiger II, whilst the two 2268kg (5000lb) thrust (with afterburning) J85-GE-21A turbojets allow a speed of Mach 1.63 for the single-seater and slightly less for the two-seat F-5F. Delivery of a very small

Above: a Northrop F-5E tactical fighter carries the markings of the Brazilian Air Force.

Below: a Northrop F-5B leads an echelon formation of F-5As in Royal Norwegian Air Force markings.

number to the USAF for combat training began in early 1973 and by mid-1981 more than 1100 had been delivered to various air forces.

Light weight is also one of the advantages of the General Dynamics F-16 Fighting Falcon, one of the latest US fighters. The first prototype flew on 2 February 1974 and eventually the F-16 was selected for USAF service after competition against the Northrop YF-17. The USAF has stated a requirement for 1388 F-16s, mostly single-seat F-16As but including more than 200 two-seat F-16B fighter-trainers. Power is provided by one 11,340kg (25,000lb) thrust (with afterburning) Pratt & Whitney F100-

PW-200 turbofan engine, giving the F-16A a maximum speed of more than Mach 2. Armament comprises a 20mm multi-barrel gun, two Sidewinders carried at the wingtips and other weapons carried on seven hardpoints.

In 1975 Belgium, Denmark, the Netherlands and Norway each decided to replace its F-104 Starfighters with F-16s. Deliveries began to Belgium in 1979. Other export Fighting Falcons were ordered by Israel, South Korea and Egypt. Israel received its first fighters in early 1980, and these were used in action in mid-1981 against Iraq's nuclear reactor at Osirak.

The fighters with variable-geometry

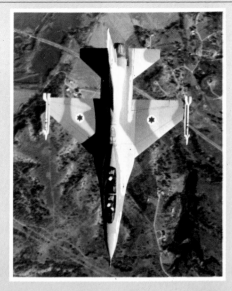

Below: a formation of F-16A Fighting Falcons of the 388th Tactical Fighter Wing, the first USAF F-16 unit.

('swing') wings that appeared during the 1970s and are now operational in large numbers or are about to become so, owe their lineage in part to the unique work carried out by General Dynamics for its F-111. This two-seat Mach 2.5 tactical strike fighter was developed for participation in the USAF's Tactical Fighter Experimental (TFX) com-

Left: an F-16B of the Israeli Air Force, which has used the Fighting Falcon in combat.

Right: F-16B two-seaters destined for the air forces of Denmark, the Netherlands, Belgium and Norway.

petition. The winner was intended to be a modern replacement for the Century Series, while also being suitable for operations from aircraft carriers, a role no doubt seen as reasonable following the F-4's compatibility to both land and sea.

Development of the swing-wings took considerable time and effort, but on 6 January 1965 the prototype F-111 varied the sweep of its wings in flight for the first time. Powered by two 8391kg (18,500lb) thrust (with afterburning) Pratt & Whitney TF30-P-1 or P-3 engines, the first production version was the USAF's F-111A, of which 141 were built. The Navy's expected F-111B was cancelled after five development and two production examples had been built. However the 'A' became basically an all-weather bomber in service from 1967. F-111C was the designation given to a version for the Royal Australian Air Force, which received 24, while Britain cancelled its expected F-111Ks. Later USAF versions have included the F-111D with improved avionics and TF30-P-9 turbofan engines, the F-111E with modified air intakes and the F-111F. Of 296 D/E/Fs built, 106 were F-111F fighter-bombers with 11,385kg (25,100lb) thrust (with afterburning) TF30-P-100 turbofans, capable of Mach 2.5 performance. Armament comprises a 20mm multi-barrel can-

Right: the USAF's General Dynamics F-111F is a low-level bomber with terrain-following capability.

Below: a prototype of the RAF's Panavia Tornado F.Mk.2, which is the Tornado air defense variant.

Above: 90 BAe Hawk T.Mk.1 jet trainers are being adapted to carry AIM-9L Sidewinders in the air defense role.

Right: the Mikoyan MiG-25 *Foxbat* is the world's fastest combat aircraft in current service.

non, plus underwing stores and bombs in the weapon bay. The first F-111Es arrived in Britain in 1970, followed by other aircraft.

Britain's own swing-wing combat plane is the Panavia Tornado, which it shares with Germany and Italy. Most of the 809 Tornados to be built for the three countries will be attack versions, but the RAF is to receive 165 Tornado ADVs (air defence variant) as Tornado F.Mk 2s, each armed with a 27mm IWKA-Mauser cannon plus four Sky Flash and two Sidewinder missiles. The two-seater is powered by two 7257kg (16,000lb) thrust (with afterburning) Turbo-Union RB.199-34R-04 turbofan engines, giving it a maximum speed of more than Mach 2. The first Tornado ADV prototype flew on 27 October 1979 and production aircraft will appear in 1983.

All of the more recent Soviet interceptors and fighter-bombers have swing-wings, with the exceptions of the Sukhoi Su-15 (NATO *Flagon*), a twin-turbojet and delta-winged Mach 2.3 single-seat interceptor, of which about 700 are operational, and the Mikoyan MiG-25 (NATO *Foxbat A*). The latter is the single-seat interceptor version of the MiG-25, powered by two 11,000kg (24,251lb) thrust (with afterburning) Tumansky R-31 turbojet engines. It carries four air-to-air missiles of *Acrid, Aphid* or *Apex* type, and has a maximum speed with missiles of Mach 2.8 (probably Mach 3.2 without missiles), making it the fastest combat aircraft in the world. Well over 300 are believed to be in use as interceptors with the Soviet air force.

The Sukhoi Su-17 (NATO *Fitter*) is basically a ground attack fighter, powered by two 11,200kg (24,692lb) thrust (with afterburning) Lyulka AL-21F-3 turbojet engines, as is the Su-20 export version and simplified export Su-22. the Sukhoi Su-24 (NATO *Fencer*) is, like the others, a variable-geometry aircraft, but for attack only.

The MiG-23 (NATO *Flogger*) has a ground attack counterpart in the MiG-27, but is itself a single-seat variable-geometry fighter. It has been built in several versions for Soviet use and export since the early 1970s and it is estimated that approximately 2000 MiG-23/27s have gone into Soviet service, with production continuing at several hundred a year. The MiG-23 is one type gradually replacing the Sukhoi Su-15.

Powered by a single 12,500kg (27,558lb) thrust Tumansky R-29B turbojet, the MiG-23MF (*Flogger-B*) is now the most important Soviet tactical fighter, displacing the MiG-21. It has a maximum speed of Mach 2.3 and is armed with one 23mm GSh-23 gun plus *Apex* or *Aphid* missiles or other weapons carried on five hardpoints.

France also developed a variable-geometry fighter as the Mirage G8, but this remained a prototype. Some years earlier Dassault moved away temporarily from its standard delta and vertical tail configuration by developing its Mirage F1, a single-seat multi-mission fighter and ground attack aircraft with swept wings and a conventional swept tail unit. The prototype first flew on 23 December 1966 but production F1-Cs did not enter French air force service until 1973. Powered by a 7,200kg (15,873lb) thrust (with afterburning) turbojet engine, the F1-C has a maximum speed of Mach 2.2. It carries two 30mm DEFA cannon plus three Matra R 530 or Super 530 and two Sidewinder or Matra 550 Magic air-to-air missiles as an interceptor. Twenty-five F1-Cs have recently been given flight refuelling capability as F1-C-200s. The only other fighter version of the F1 is the F1-E, with improved avionics. By 1981 nearly 400 F1s had been built, including many for export.

The very latest French fighters are the Mirage 2000 and the Super Mirage 4000, both returning to Dassault's trusted delta wing form. The former is basically a single-seat interceptor and air superiority fighter, powered by a SNECMA M53 turbofan engine. The first prototype flew on 10

Above: a Sukhoi Su-20 ground-attack fighter is pictured in service with the Egyptian air force.

Left: the Mikoyan MiG-23 *Flogger* is the Soviet Union's most important tactical fighter aircraft.

Right: a French Mirage F1 is armed with ground attack weapons. It also serves as an interceptor aircraft.

Above left: a two-seat Mirage G8 formates on a single-seat version of this variable-geometry fighter.

Above: a Dassault Mirage F1-E interceptor carries wingtip-mounted air-to-air missiles.

Left: Mirage F1 fighters (foreground) pictured on the production line shortly before rollout.

Right: three Mirage 2000 prototypes fly in formation with the larger, twin-engined Super Mirage 4000.

March 1978 and delivery of the first single-seaters and two-seat trainers will begin in 1983. Typical armament will comprise two 30mm DEFA cannon plus two Super 530 and two Magic missiles. A prototype two-seat low-level penetration version of the Mirage 2000 will fly in 1983 as the Mirage 2000N.

A considerably larger aircraft is the Super Mirage 4000, first flown on 9 March 1979. Powered by two M53 engines, it too is a single-seater but is designated a multi-role combat type. It is likely that this aircraft has a maximum speed similar to the Mirage 2000's Mach 2.2.

In September 1969 Israel flew the prototype of an indigenous fighter based on the French Mirage III/5. This became the Nesher, about 40 of which entered Israeli service from 1972. From the Nesher IAI developed the Kfir-C1, which flew in prototype form in 1973. This delta-winged fighter is powered by an 8,120kg (17,902lb) thrust (with afterburning) General Electric J79-J1E turbojet engine and possesses a maximum speed of more than Mach 2.

From the Kfir-C1 was developed the Kfir-C2, the most obvious external difference being the use of small canards. This improved Kfir entered service during the mid-1970s. Earlier-built Kfirs are being updated to C2 standard, in which form maneuverability and take off/landing performance is improved. About 200 Kfirs have been built, each armed with two 30mm cannon and two Shafrir air-to-air missiles or ground attack weapons.

Saab's most recent interceptor for the Swedish air force is the JA 37 Viggen, just one of five versions of the Saab-37 that have been built. The Viggen first flew as a prototype on 8 February 1967, production eventually starting with the AJ 37 single-seat attack variant. The single-seat JA 37 has been delivered as a Draken replacement since 1979, but this too has attack capability. The Swedish air force expects to receive 149 JA 37s by 1985, each powered by a single 12,750kg (28,100lb) thrust (with after-

Left: Israel Aircraft Industries developed the Kfir-C1 fighter from the French Dassault Mirage III/5.

Above: the IAI Kfir-C2 is fitted with small canard foreplanes, which enhance maneuverability.

burning) Volvo Flygmotor RM8B turbofan engine, bestowing a maximum speed of Mach 2 plus. Easily recognizable by its tandem delta-type wings and canards, the JA 37 can be armed with one 30mm Oerlikon cannon and six Sky Flash and Sidewinder missiles.

India became one of the select band of countries to develop and produce a supersonic fighter in May 1964, when the Indian Air Force took delivery of its first HAL HF-24 Marut attack fighters. Powered by two 2200kg (4850lb) thrust HAL-built Rolls-Royce Bristol Orpheus 703 turbojet engines, allowing a maximum speed of 1,112km/h (691mph), the single-seat Maruts can each carry four 30mm Aden guns and an underfuselage retractable pack of fifty SNEB 68mm air-to-air rockets, plus ground attack

weapons under the wings.

Japan also joined the select band when Mitsubishi produced its F-1. This was developed as a close-support fighter from the earlier T-2 two-seat trainer, the first prototype flying on 3 June 1975. Production aircraft have been delivered to the JASDF since September 1977 and by early 1981 deliveries amounted to 57 of the 67 so far ordered. Each F-1 is powered by two 3207kg (7070lb) thrust (with afterburning) Japanese-built Adour turbofan engines, known as TF40-IHI-801As, giving a Mach 1.6 performance. Armament comprises one 20mm JM61 multi-barrel cannon plus four Sidewinders or ground attack weapons.

Romania and Yugoslavia joined forces to produce their first supersonic combat plane, a single-seat tactical fighter known

as the CNIAR IAR-93 and SOKO Orao respectively. First flown as a prototype on 31 October 1974, the production version is powered by two 2270kg (5000lb) thrust (with afterburning) Rolls-Royce Viper Mk

Above: a Saab JA 37 Viggen interceptor is pictured carrying Sidewinder and Sky Flash air-to-air missiles.

Left: Viggen pilots of the Swedish air force's F 13 Wing pose on the flightline in front of their aircraft.

Left: the Mitsubishi F-1 close-support fighter was developed from the earlier T-2 two-seat training aircraft.

632 turbojet engines and can achieve a speed of 1130km/h (702mph). Each nation is expected to receive about 200 aircraft, including two-seat training examples, each armed with two 23mm cannon.

Development of jet fighters never stops. As one new fighter enters production so another leaves the drawing board: a pattern of events repeated in many countries.

In the United States, General Dynamics is developing an advanced version of its F-16 and Northrop a version of its F-5 as the F-5G Tigershark, while in the Soviet Union Mikoyan is reportedly flight testing a new Mach 2 plus fighter roughly equivalent to the US Hornet. In China the Mach 2 plus Shenyang J-8 is under development, while designs for lightweight multi-role types have appeared in Sweden and Switzerland, as the JAS/Saab 2105 and ALR Piranha respectively, both of these with rear-mounted main wings and canards. The jet fighter story has no immediate end, just a point at which no further information is available!

INDEX

ACKNOWLEDGMENTS

Photographs from the author's collection except as listed below.

Picture Acknowledgments

Air BP: p 8
Air Portraits: pp 65, 66
Austin J. Brown: pp 94 (bottom), 119
Denis Hughes: pp 111, 115, 116, 117, 150-51
MAP: pp 116-17
Royal Air Force Museum, Hendon: pp 6-7, 12-13, 20-21, 95
Matthew Nathan: pp 9, 10 (both), 11, 19, 22-23
Bob Snyder: pp 17, 26-27, 30, 30-31, 52-53, 56 (top), 97, 128-29
Gordon S Williams: pp 44-45
USAF: pp 34, 36, 36-37, 48
US Navy: pp 70-71, 75